S0-AUA-554

Uncle Arthur's
BEDTIME STORIES
Volume Two

Uncle Arthur's Bedtime STORIES

Volume Two/Arthur S. Maxwell

Published jointly by
Pacific Press Publishing Association
Mountain View, Calif., Omaha, Nebr., Oshawa, Ont.
Review and Herald Publishing Association
Washington, D.C.
Southern Publishing Association
Nashville, Tennessee

PAINTING BY ROBERT L. BERRAN, © BY REVIEW AND HERALD

Copyright © 1976 by the
Review and Herald Publishing Association
Washington, D.C.
Library of Congress Catalog Card No. 74-83676

Copyright © 1964, 1965, 1966, 1967 by the Review and Herald
Publishing Association.
All rights reserved. No part of its literary or pictorial contents
may be reproduced without permission from the publishers.

Printed in U.S.A.

Contents

6

Lesson Index

7

Artists participating in the illustration of this volume are: Harry Anderson, Harry Baerg, Robert L. Berran, Fred Collins, Kreigh Collins, Gib Crockett, Wm. Dolwick, Arlo Greer, Russell Harlan, William Heaslip, Wm. M. Hutchinson, Manning de V. Lee, Donald Muth, Vernon Nye, Peter J. Rennings, Herbert Rudeen, H. Sonderman, and Jack White. Cover by John Steel.

The Bird With the Kindly Heart

HERE IS THE PRETTIEST bird story I think I have ever heard. It's about a little chaffinch that lived at Saundersfoot in Pembrokeshire, Wales.

Saundersfoot, by the way, is a little seaside village, with just a few old-fashioned houses and a delightful stretch of sandy beach. A long lane, running between flower-decked hedgerows, separates it from the nearest railway station. I know, because I went there once in search of a friend—and found he had left two hours before I got there! I also missed the chaffinch, and of that I am more sorry still.

One stormy day not very long ago this little bird, wearied perhaps by the wind, flew through an open window into one of the houses in the village.

Now it so happened that in the room was a little invalid girl, Kathleen by name, who was delighted to see her little visitor. She gave it some food and cared for it tenderly all night till the storm was over. Then in the morning the chaffinch flew away.

But the next day, to Kathleen's surprise and delight, it returned, took some food, and flew away again! The next day it

9

◀ Painting by Manning de V. Lee © by Review and Herald

One day while Kathleen was fast asleep the friendly little bird quietly flew into the room and dropped a red ribbon on her hair.

10   did the same, and for quite a time not a morning passed without the chaffinch's coming for its breakfast.

Then one day the visits ceased. Poor Kathleen thought the bird must surely have been killed. She waited and waited, keeping some food close to the window, but in vain.

A week later, however, the chaffinch came again, but with a wound in its little breast. Kathleen was very sorry for it and nursed it till it was well again, watching it eat from a tiny tray on her bed. They became fast friends.

Then an extraordinary thing happened. One day Kathleen's aunt came into the room while the little girl was asleep, and saw a strange piece of pink ribbon lying on her hair. She wondered how it could have gotten there. Kathleen, when she awoke, said she knew nothing about it.

As they were talking about it, what do you suppose happened? In through the open window flew the chaffinch with another little gift in its beak, this time a brightly colored piece of wool yarn. It dropped the yarn on the pillow and flew away.

"Oh, you dear, kindhearted little bird," cried Kathleen. "You're trying to say, Thank you!"

And as I heard the story I thought of the Master's words, "She hath done what she could!"

STORY **2**

Sylvia's Glasses

IF THERE WAS ONE thing Sylvia hoped she would *never* have to do, it was to wear glasses. Secretly she despised girls who had to wear them. She thought that glasses spoiled their looks and made them plain and homely. Many times as she looked in the mirror at her own pretty features she thought that to have to wear glasses would be the worst thing that could happen to her.

Then one day the blow fell. All joy vanished from her life. She thought she could never be happy again. Teacher had sent her home from school with a note saying that she should have her eyes tested; she was holding her books too close to her face!

"Don't look so worried," said Mother, after she had read the note. "It isn't any trouble to have one's eyes tested, and it doesn't hurt, you know."

"But, Mother," cried Sylvia, "you don't think I will have to wear glasses, do you? I couldn't. I simply couldn't."

"Well, we don't know, do we?" said Mother. "Let's go and find out. That's the wise thing to do."

So off they went to an optometrist. He was kind and gen-

11

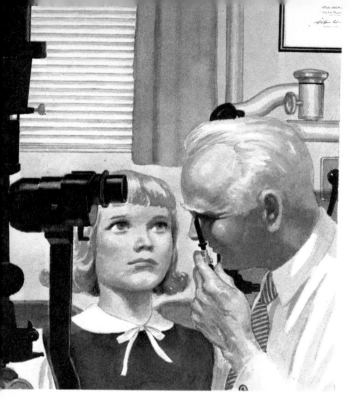

tle, and smilingly tested Sylvia's eyes with the wonderful instruments in his office. Sylvia had to admit that it didn't hurt at all, but her worry increased as he continued to put little pieces of glass in front of her eyes, asking whether she could see better with this or with that. All along she had hoped that he would tell her that her eyes were perfectly all right, or just a little tired, needing only a short rest. Now here he was trying glasses on her eyes as though she had to have them anyway!

The examination completed, the optometrist turned to Mother and broke the news. "She certainly does need glasses," he said, "and she should have had them sometime ago. I can have them ready for her in a few days. I'll contact you about them."

Mother agreed, and they left, with Sylvia trailing behind, her face red with anger.

"I won't wear them, Mother! I won't, I tell you!"

"But, Sylvia, you need them," said Mother gently. "They will help you so much. I believe you will be able to learn your lessons easier, and maybe you won't get so many headaches."

"I don't care!" said Sylvia. "I'd rather have headaches than wear nasty old glasses. They will make me look so old and homely."

"Oh, you shouldn't be thinking about that," said Mother, smiling. "Your health is far more important than your looks. Anyway, you won't look too bad in glasses, Sylvia."

But Sylvia was not to be comforted. She had made up her mind that she was going to hate glasses, that she wouldn't wear them, and that was that.

"I wish I could get hold of the person who invented glasses!" she said bitterly. "I'd—I'd——"

"That would be rather difficult," said Mother. "You would have to travel a long, long way. Hundreds of miles and hundreds of years. The Chinese are supposed to be the first to have worn them. Their great hero Confucius tells in his writings how he gave a pair to a poor cobbler. That was about 500 B.C. Another story from China tells of a rich man who gave one of his finest horses for a pair of glasses around A.D. 1260. But those glasses may have been just ornaments."

"Ornaments!" snorted Sylvia. "Fancy wearing the horrid things as ornaments!"

"Oh, many people have done that," said Mother. "But usually, of course, they are worn only as a help to the eyes. The man who gets the credit for this idea is Roger Bacon, who wrote about them in A.D. 1276, saying that they were useful to those 'who are old and have weak sight.'"

"But I'm not old," said Sylvia.

"Not very," smiled Mother, "but evidently you do have weak sight. But let me finish the story of glasses. The first maker of them in Europe is believed to have been an Italian called Salvino D'Armato of Florence. We know this because of the words on his tombstone in one of the big old churches in that city: 'Here lies Salvino D'Armato, of the Amati of

Florence. Inventor of spectacles. God pardon him for his sins.
A.D. 1317.'"

"His sins?" inquired Sylvia. "Making spectacles, maybe."

"No," said Mother laughing, "not that. His work proved a great blessing to many people. For many years after that, spectaclemaking was a trade, like shoemaking or carpentry. Lenses were ground, fitted into frames, and sold on the streets. The buyer selected the pair that suited him. There

were then no optometrists to test people's eyes as yours were tested."

At last the optometrist telephoned to say the glasses were ready. Sylvia and her mother went to his shop and he carefully slipped the spectacles on the reluctant girl. At once Sylvia noticed how clear everything was about her. She picked up a book and saw how easy it was to read.

"Why, Mother," she said, "these things make everything different. All the world seems new!"

And the world was new—to her. She had never seen it properly before. She had not realized what a burden she was carrying, nor what darkness she had been living in so long.

So thrilled was Sylvia at the clear vision she now had that she actually forgot to look in the mirror. That is, for an hour or two. Then, when she did look she had another surprise. "Why!" she exclaimed, "I don't look so bad in them after all!"

◄ Painting by H. Sonderman. Courtesy, Bausch and Lomb Optical Co.

When glasses first became available there were no optometrists to test your eyes. You chose the glasses you thought helped you most.

STORY **3**

Love,
Not War

SUCH A NOISE as there was in the back yard! You never heard anything like it—at least I hope you never did.

Bert and Bob had been playing Indians around the little summerhouse at the end of the lawn. Bob was dressed up as a chief with feathers he had saved from the chicken house, and Bert was supposed to be the white man trying to keep him from getting into the summerhouse.

Then had come the quarrel. Bob said that Bert was dead, because he had shot him with his bow and arrow; but Bert said that he wasn't dead and wasn't going to be dead for Bob or anybody else.

"You're a cheat," cried Bob; "you are dead!"

"I'm not a cheat, and I'm not dead!" cried Bert.

"You are."

"I'm not."

"You are."

"I'm not."

"I won't play anymore."

"Don't play then; play by yourself."

Both boys got more and more angry, and presently Bob hit Bert on the nose. Then there was a tussle, in the midst of which a voice was heard from the dining room window.

"Come in, come in, both of you," cried Mother. "I won't have this noise in the yard. What will the neighbors think of you?"

Sullenly the two boys walked toward the house.

"It was his fault," said Bert.

"Wasn't; it was Bert's," said Bob.

"You started it."

"I didn't."

"Never mind; come along, both of you, and sit on these two chairs. And not a sound from either of you for the next quarter of an hour."

Bob and Bert sat down at opposite sides of the room and glared at each other in silence. For when Mother said they were not to talk, she meant it.

Very slowly the minutes ticked away. The boys thought they had never sat still so long before.

Just before the quarter of an hour was up, Mother came into the room again.

"I'm going to tell you a little story," she said. Their faces brightened.

"Many years ago," began Mother, "when Indians used to roam over the wide plains and forests of North America, there used to be terrible fights between them and the white people who were trying to settle in America. The Indians naturally felt that the country belonged to them and that the white people had no right to it. So they fought to keep what was theirs. Many of the white people were very cruel, and this only made matters worse.

"Then one day a man landed in America determined to try a different method with the Indians. His name was William Penn, and he thought he would seek to make friends with them instead of fighting them. He told his people at home that he was going to give them perfect justice and show them all respect and friendliness. Of course, they laughed at him and said that he would be tomahawked and scalped in no time, but he kept his resolve."

"Didn't he take a gun with him?" asked Bert.

"Your silence period isn't up yet," said Mother.

"Oh," grunted Bert, subsiding.

"No, he didn't take a gun with him," Mother went on. "And soon after he arrived in the new country he called all the Indians together, because he wanted to talk with them. They came in large numbers, in all their war paint, and carrying their arms. Probably they suspected a trap. Penn met them with a few friends, all unarmed. Then he talked to them as no white man had ever spoken to them before. 'We must use no weapons against our fellow creatures,' he said. 'Good faith and good will toward man are our defenses. We believe you will deal kindly and justly by us, and we will deal kindly and justly by you. We meet on the broad highway of faith and good will; no advantage shall be taken on either side, but all shall be openness and love, for we are all one flesh and blood.'

"After he had finished speaking Penn pulled out of his pocket a piece of paper on which he had drawn up a treaty to be signed by the Indians and himself. He read it over to them, while they listened with astonishment. This is how part of the agreement read:

" 'We will be brethren, my people and your people, as the children of one Father. All the paths shall be open to the Christian and the Indian. The doors of the Christian shall be open to the Indian, and the wigwams of the Indian shall be open to the Christian.' Most of the white people who heard about it said Penn was foolish. But the Indian chiefs agreed to the treaty, gave Penn a pledge of good faith, and went away content.

"Time went on, and while in other parts of America there was constant fighting, in Pennsylvania—that part of the country which was named after Penn—there was peace. When Penn wanted land from the Indians, he bought it. He insisted that if a white man injured an Indian, he must be punished just the same as if he had injured a white man, and that the white people must not sell bad goods to the Indians when trading with them. Everybody had to give them fair play."

"And wasn't he ever scalped?" asked Bob, with one eye on the clock.

"No, indeed," said Mother. "The Indians loved him too much for that. And for forty years no unarmed man was killed in Pennsylvania. So you see, by treating the Indians kindly he won their friendship and kept peace. It's too bad that the whites in general didn't follow his example."

Bob and Bert were fast cooling down now.

"I suppose, then," said Bert, "that I should make peace with that Indian over there."

"It would certainly be a very nice thing to do," said Mother.

"Time's up," cried Bob, looking at the clock again. And with happy smiles they both slid off their chairs and ran out into the yard.

◄ Painting by Herbert Rudeen © by Review and Herald

William Penn went unarmed to the Indians, spoke kindly to them, and made peace with them. They learned to trust each other.

4

The Worth
of a Smile

HOW MUCH IS A SMILE WORTH? A penny? A quarter? A hundred dollars?

Well, it's worth something, isn't it?

It surely is, but somehow you could never fix a price for a smile, could you? To do so would spoil its value at once.

Yet sometimes a smile is very valuable.

Many years ago there lived on one of the very poor streets of New York a little girl called Hannah. She was eleven years old and her cheerful little face often brought gladness to sad people who saw her on the street.

One day Hannah went to a children's program at a nearby church. She had been there many times before to attend meetings of various kinds; but this time she was to take part in a program herself. You can imagine how pleased she was about it.

Now, it so happened that in the audience that afternoon was a well-known doctor, one of the supporters of that church. Whether or not he was feeling lonely or sad that day will never be known, but somehow as he looked at Hannah's dear little face, his heart was touched. Then she turned and

23

◄ Color Photo by H. A. Roberts

What gives a smile its value? Its beauty? Its friendliness? Its sincerity? Or is it the effect it has upon another?

24 looked straight at him and smiled! He thought he had never seen anything so lovely before. He left the hall a happier and better man.

And he never forgot that smile. It lived with him every day until he died.

When his will was read, his executors were astonished to learn that he had left all his money—and he was a very rich man—not to any relatives, for he had none; not to any hospital or mission, as he might have done, but, using his own words, "to those who have given me happiness during my lifetime."

On the list was Hannah's name, the little girl who had smiled at him in the church program twenty years before. He left her $150,000!

Think of that—$150,000 for a smile!

I can almost hear you saying, "I wish my smiles were worth as much as that." They are! But not in money.

Think of the happiness they bring to Mother and Father. Your smiles help them bear their burdens more easily, and make them live longer, too. Isn't that worth something?

Smiles make the wheels of a home move so much more smoothly, while frowns and scowls and pouts are like sand and gravel thrown into the works.

Who does not love the boy or girl who smiles when things go wrong—when other children annoy them or they are hurt while playing games? Such smiles are worth much more than money.

Suppose you smile someday at someone who is very sad and discouraged, and make him smile, too; what is that worth? You may never know, but it may mean everything to him—the turning of a corner on life's dark and lonely road. And there are lots of people today like this, people who have given up hope that anybody will smile at them again. As the familiar hymn says—

> "There are hearts that are drooping in sorrow
>   today,
>   There are souls under shadow the while;
> Oh, the comfort from God you can gently
>   convey,
>   And brighten the way with a smile!"

Won't you try to see how much good you can do with your smiles? You will be repaid in happiness untold.

Just-a-Minute Janet

"JANET! JANET!" her mother called. She waited a moment, but there was no reply.

"Hoo-hoo, Janet!" Mother called again, going to the kitchen window, trying to see what Janet was doing.

"Just a minute, Mommy," came a little voice from the back yard. "I won't be long."

"But I'm waiting for you," called Mother. "I want you to come now."

"Just a minute," answered the invisible Janet.

"Dear me!" exclaimed Mother to herself. "How tired I am of hearing her say, 'Just a minute.' Wait till she comes in!"

Five minutes passed. Then ten minutes. But no Janet appeared.

"Janet!" called Mother, going to the window again. "Come here at once!"

"Just a minute!"

"Oh!" said Mother, "if I don't——"

But at this moment Janet's little face smiling so sweetly popped around the corner of the tool shed so that Mother didn't know what to say next.

"Here I am," said Janet pleasantly. "Did you call, Mommy?"

"You heard me call," said Mother, trying to look stern. "Why didn't you come at once?"

"I was busy," replied Janet demurely. "You see, I was washing dolly's clothes."

"Maybe you were," said Mother, "but when your mother calls, you must obey at once. It's very rude to keep Mommy waiting ten whole minutes before you come to her."

"Yes, Mommy," said Janet.

"And don't you ever say, 'Just a minute,' again."

"No, Mommy."

"All right," said Mother. "Now take these eggs around to Mrs. Jones."

Janet took the package and ran off happily, humming a little tune to herself. But while she was gone she quite forgot all that her mother had said.

When she returned she went out into the yard again to her "washtub" behind the shed. Oh, what fun it was rubbing and scrubbing and making soapsuds just like Mommy! And she had a clothesline all for herself, some of Mommy's clothespins, and a real scrubbing board. No wonder she was happy!

28 But by and by a familiar voice was heard again. "Janet! Janet!"

The reply was equally familiar.

"Just a minute, Mommy!"

"So she has forgotten already," said Mother. "Then she will have to learn some other way."

Once more the minutes passed—five minutes, ten minutes, fifteen minutes. Still no sign of Janet.

But meanwhile Mother went on with her dinner, and when she had finished, cleared the table. She was half repenting of her decision when an unusual sound caught her ears.

"Oh, Mommy, Mommy! Come quick! come quick! The water's spilled all over me!"

Suddenly a bright idea came to Mommy. Feeling sure that nothing serious had happened, she called out:

"Just a minute, Janet!"

"Oh, come quick! come quick!" wailed Janet; "my shoes are full of water!"

Mother did not stir. She merely called back once more, very deliberately.

"Just a minute, Janet."

At this the poor, soaked Janet appeared around the corner. What a sight she was! As she had jumped off the stool after hanging dolly's dress on her line, she had tipped the tubful of water on top of herself.

Mother couldn't help laughing.

"Why didn't you come when I called?" said Janet very crossly. "Can't you see I'm all wet and messy?"

"I couldn't," said Mother. "You see, I was busy. I had to clear the table after dinner."

"Is it as late as that?" asked Janet, looking surprised.

"Yes," said Mother. "If you had come when I called this wouldn't have happened."

Janet saw the point, and a faint little smile flickered across her face. And, of course, that was the end of it; for Mother ran to get her some dry clothes *and* some dinner, while Janet promised once more that she really never would keep Mommy waiting again.

STORY **6**

Four
Chocolate Eggs

WHAT EXCITEMENT THERE WAS in the classroom that morning! What eagerness and attention!

You see, the teacher had just announced that she was going to give a small gift to the boy or girl who answered the most questions correctly in the tests they were going to have that day.

What it was, she wouldn't say, except that it was very nice, very pretty, and very tasty.

Of course that last word set everybody's mouth watering.

"Something tasty!" said Ted Jones. "I could use that right now."

"And so could I," said Eric Foster, whose mother had been
so busy that morning looking after his two little brothers and
his baby sister that she had forgotten to make his lunch.

"But I would rather have something pretty," said Peggy
Phillips, just like a girl.

"I wonder where she put it," said Peter Rich. "Perhaps we
could take a peep at it when she's not looking."

The teacher heard that.

"Oh, no, you can't," she said. "It is put away safely in my
desk, and no one will see it until the tests are all over."

Peter blushed and wished he hadn't spoken.

Then the tests began, and how everyone did work! When
the teacher asked the questions aloud, hands flashed up all
over the room and waved about like trees in a high wind.
When the answers had to be written, there was an unusual
silence.

It was lots of fun, and everyone had high hopes of winning
the prize.

Slowly the hours dragged by, with Ted and Peter and
Peggy and all the rest becoming more and more certain that
they were going to win, and poor Eric getting hungrier and
hungrier every minute and imagining what he would do with
the prize if he should win.

At last the tests were all over, the answers all checked,
and the final marks all totaled up.

Who had won?

"Now," said the teacher, "I'm almost ready to tell you who
has won the prize."

The silence was so deep that you could have heard a pin
drop.

"It's going to be me," whispered Peter to Peggy.

The teacher heard again. What good ears some teachers
do have!

"I'm afraid you are wrong, Peter," she said. "The prize
goes to——"

"Peggy," "Ted," "Tommy," "Dick," "Amy," "Dora," came a
chorus from all over the room.

"No," said the teacher, smiling, "you're all wrong. Eric is
the winner, beating Peggy by just one mark." Peggy groaned.

At this moment the teacher opened her desk and produced
a big chocolate egg, tied with a piece of wide blue ribbon.

"How lovely!" cried everybody. "Lucky boy!" said Ted.

"Now just a moment," said teacher. "I have a second prize.
It is in this box."

Everyone looked and saw four little chocolate eggs. They
were good, too, but not as attractive as the big one in the blue
ribbon.

Eric, blushing, came forward to receive his prize. He had
looked at both prizes and was thinking hard.

The teacher smiled at him and told him how pleased she
was that he had done so well. Then she proceeded to hand
him the big chocolate egg. But Eric's hands were behind his
back, his face scarlet.

◄ Painting by Russell Harlan

**"Please," Eric stammered, "would—would you
mind if I had the second prize instead?"**

"Please," he stammered, "would—would you mind if I had the second prize instead?"

Everybody gasped, and the teacher was so surprised that she hardly knew what to say. She had thought there wasn't a child in the room who would not have been thrilled to take the beautiful gift she was offering. "But," she thought, "Eric is always a good boy, and he must have a reason for his unusual request." So she gave him the second prize, and Peggy was surely delighted to get the first prize after all.

Of course, every boy and girl in the class wanted to know why Eric had done such a strange thing, but he wouldn't say a word. He just ran home with his precious box under his arm, not even opening it to take one nibble.

But if any of Eric's school friends could have peeped inside his home that evening, they would have found out all about it. For there, sitting on the kitchen floor, were four of the happiest children you could imagine. Just three boys and one baby girl.

And they were all munching chocolate eggs.

7

The Book That Would Not Burn

HOW BETTY LOVED her daddy! And somehow, even though she had seven brothers and sisters, she felt that her daddy loved her best of all. Perhaps that was because she was the eldest in the family and so, of course, Daddy had had longer to love her than all the rest.

Daddy, by the way, was a minister, and among his most precious possessions was a Bible that a very dear friend had given him many years ago. He always used this Bible when he was studying, or preaching, and, of course, in family worship.

One day when Betty and her daddy were alone in his study, he suddenly became very solemn.

"Betty," he said quietly, "none of us knows what is going to happen in the future, but if anything should go wrong—er—if anything should happen to me——"

"Don't say that, Daddy," said Betty, with a worried look on her face. "Nothing must ever happen to you."

"Of course, we hope not," replied Daddy with a smile, "but just in case something sometime should happen to me, I want you to have my Bible. It is to be yours, always."

35

"Oh, thank you, Daddy," cried Betty. "I shall prize it above everything else all my life."

From that day on, even though Daddy continued to use his Bible as he always had, Betty watched over it with special care. Every now and then she would go into the study and dust the Book tenderly, then open it to read some message for herself. She felt that it was her Book already, and that it would be a precious memory of her father forever.

Not long after this, Daddy fell ill. Month after month went by, and he became steadily worse. Then one day he said good-by to everybody and passed away.

Betty was heartbroken, and her only consolation was the thought that Daddy had given her his Bible, his most precious possession. She left it there on his study table, where it lay surrounded by all the other books in the library, like a king amid his courtiers. Every day she would tiptoe into the room and touch it reverently, silently turning its sacred pages. Tears would come to her eyes as she remembered that this was *his* Book and that he had given it to her.

Then one day something dreadful happened.

Betty was visiting in the home of a girl friend across the road. While they were talking together, they heard the fire alarm, and one said to the other, "There must be a fire somewhere; I wonder whose house it is this time?"

They went to the window to look out, and suddenly Betty screamed.

"It's our house!" she cried. "Oh, look at the flames!"

They ran outside and tried to cross the road, but already a large crowd had gathered, and two fire engines were busy pumping water on the flames, while helmeted firemen were smashing windows and trying to carry out what furniture they could.

Betty struggled to break through the crowd, but the neighbors held her back. She appealed to the policeman to let her run into the burning house.

◀ Painting by Russell Harlan © by Review and Herald

Every day Betty would tiptoe into the room and reverently turn the pages of Daddy's Bible.

"There's something in there I've got to save!" she cried, beside herself with anxiety.

"But, child," he said, "you can't go in there. It's just a roaring furnace. You'd be burned to a cinder."

"But I've got to go!" cried Betty. "I've got to go! Let me go!"

"No, dear. I couldn't let you go in there," said the kindly policeman. "I'm sorry, but it's impossible. See, even the firemen are leaving now."

Betty turned away heartbroken. It was of no use. Of course it was of no use. She could see that. But, oh, her Bible! If only she had stayed at home!

Away in the crowd, yet feeling more alone than she had ever felt in all her life, she thought of Jesus.

"O Lord," she cried, wringing her hands, "save my Bible, Daddy's Bible. Don't let it burn. Please don't let it get burned!"

And so she prayed, while the angry flames roared through the building, turning the home she loved so dearly into a heap of ugly ashes. Two hours after the fire had begun there

was nothing left but two gaunt chimneys and some black-ened, smoldering timbers. Roof, bedrooms, dining room, kitchen, living room—all had vanished.

It was some time after this before even members of the family were allowed to wander through the ruins, but Betty was among the first. She hurried to where the study had been. She knew the place well, and it was still clearly marked by remnants of half-burned books that had belonged to her father's library.

What a terrible sight! What would dear Daddy have said!

She came to some charred pieces of wood that she recognized had once been a desk, *his* desk. With more tenderness than ever, she moved them and peered beneath.

She gasped. What on earth was that? Could it be? Could it possibly be?

Yes, it was. Her Bible. Daddy's Bible!

With a cry of joy she picked it up and turned its pages with an eagerness she had never shown before.

There was not a mark of fire upon it, not the shadow of a burn upon the cover or the inside!

I know it is true. Betty herself told me about it. And she told me something else. She said that that Book of hers, so marvelously preserved in the fire, became the center of the new home that the family finally built. All the children turned to it as never before. They listened to its message as they never had in all their lives. All of them gave their hearts to God. And even today, though they have all grown up and scattered over the world, whenever they come back home, they gaze once more upon the Bible that was saved from the fire. the wonderful Book that would not burn.

STORY **8**

Weeding the Walk

FROM THE FRONT DOOR to the front gate, the gravel walk was in a dreadful state. Grass and weeds of all kinds were growing out of the gravel. A passer-by might well have supposed that no one lived in the house anymore.

But he would have been mistaken. The house *was* inhabited—very much so, only most of the people who lived in it preferred playing games to weeding walks.

One day Father thought it was about time something should be done about those weeds. "This afternoon," he said to his four children, "we are all going to weed the front walk. It is a positive disgrace to the neighborhood."

As he spoke, gloom settled upon the whole household.

"That job would take all night," said Gerald.

"Anyhow, I can't do any weeding," said Philip, "because I have to play football this afternoon."

"And I'm meeting my friend Edith," said Eva, "so I can't possibly do any."

"And I just hate weeding," said Ralph, the youngest.

"But this walk is going to be weeded this afternoon," said
40 Father. "I am tired of your excuses. Surely we must all help

to keep our own entrance tidy."

"Why don't you concrete it over?" asked Gerald.

"I'd be delighted to," replied Father, "if you would pay the bill. It would cost about $300."

"Whew!" said Philip. "I wouldn't give $300 to make a front walk."

"That's why we are all going to weed the one we have," said Father.

"Ugh! I hate weeding," repeated Ralph.

"So do I," echoed Gerald; "and if we begin, we shall have to spend hours on it. There's a week's work there."

"But you said just now," said Father, "that it would take only one night."

"That was a mistake," said Gerald. "I should have said it would take a month."

"Well, the longer we sit here the more time we'll think it's going to take," said Father. "Personally, I think that if we all put our backs to it, we can be done in less than an hour and a half."

"Phew! I don't," said Philip.

"Nor do I," said Ralph.

"Well, anyway, we will make an attempt at it," said Father. "I have a plan in my mind as to how it can be done. I will divide the walk into five portions, and we will each take one. Ralph will have a smaller one than the rest of us, because he's not so old. Then I'll offer two prizes. The first will be a prize of one dollar to the first who clears his patch completely, and the second a prize of fifty cents to the first who fills his bucket full of weeds. There will be twenty-five cents a bucketful to the rest. Now what do you think of that?"

"Not a bad idea, Father," said Gerald.

"When should we begin?" asked Philip.

"I'm going to begin on mine now," said Ralph, making a rush for the door.

"Oh, no, you don't," said Eva. "That's not fair. We've all

got to begin together, if it's a race."

"Well, Father, hurry up and mark it out, so we can begin," urged Philip. "I want that first prize."

"I will," replied Father. "I won't be more than five minutes. Meanwhile you get a bucket each and a pointed stick or a potato knife to help you get the weeds out without tearing up the gravel."

"Yippee!" they all cried, while Father hurried out to divide the walk into sections.

"Now I want you all to look at the clock," he said, as he reentered the room. "It is now two minutes to three. We will all begin together at three o'clock. We won't stop till the job's finished, and then we'll come in here and see how long it has taken. Are you all ready? One—two—three—go!"

Away they all went, and in less than a minute the weeds were flying into the pails.

Not a word was spoken, though an occasional grunt told of an obstinate weed that refused to come up at the first attempt. Five minutes passed, ten minutes, fifteen minutes. Then a triumphant yell from Philip told that his pail was full, "pressed down and running over."

"Twenty-five cents for the next one full," cried Father.

Flip, flip, flip, up came the weeds. Gerald won the next prize, and Eva the third.

Though the children were too busy to notice, the path was rapidly being cleared.

An hour passed, then an hour and fifteen minutes.

"Finished!" cried Ralph.

The others looked around in amazement. The little fellow had done it indeed. There wasn't a weed to be seen in his part of the path.

"Well done, buddy!" cried Gerald, "I won't be far behind you."

He wasn't. Five minutes later he, too, was finished. Then came Eva, and finally Philip. Before half past four they were all in the dining room.

"Would you mind looking at the clock?" said Father, smiling and rubbing his fingers, which were both sore and dirty. "I thought somebody said that it was going to take a month."

"What about the prizes?" said Philip.

"I have them," said Father. "And this just shows what can be done when everybody helps," he added, as with due ceremony he handed out the cash.

STORY **9**

In His Steps

THE STANFORDS LIVED on a farm in Maine where, in winter, it becomes very cold and the snowfall is sometimes several feet in depth.

One morning as the family came downstairs they noticed that the kitchen was very dark. Someone pulled up the blind, but it made little difference.

"Why," said one of the boys, "the snow is actually above the window!"

And so it was. They all ran into the other rooms and found that the windows on one side of the house were quite blocked up, while even beneath the others there was a great deal of snow.

Ned and Bessie, who were there on a visit, were rather frightened.

"How shall we get to school this morning?" asked Ned. "We'll never be able to walk through this, will we, Mr. Stanford?"

"We can't even open the front door," said Bessie. But the others only smiled.

44   "Oh, yes, we can," said Mr. Stanford, "but we'll all have to

work hard to clear a way out."

They all took spades or shovels and it was not long before they had cut a path through the drift that covered the front yard. Now all around them was a sea of white, stretching as far as the eye could reach, broken only by occasional trees and buildings in the distance. The schoolhouse, about a mile away, was just in sight, covered, like everything else, with a thick mantle of snow. It had never looked so far away.

"I don't see how we are going to get there even now," said Ned. "The snow is too soft to walk on. We would sink up to our necks in it."

"Wait and see," said Mr. Stanford, "you will get to school all right. Don't worry. This isn't the first time it has snowed here."

The time to start for school came a little earlier than usual, because of the snow.

"Follow me," said Mr. Stanford. "Put your feet exactly where I place mine, and you will be quite all right. See?"

With that he started forward, his big boots sinking deep in the snow, but making a hard path on which the children could walk in safety.

Ned and Bess and the others followed. They put their little legs down into the deep holes made by Mr. Stanford's boots and trudged on toward the school. It was very slow going because the holes were so deep that it was a job to get out of them again, once you got in, especially for anyone with short legs. But Mr. Stanford strode forward, and the children hopped along behind him, until at last the schoolhouse was reached.

"So you see we got here all right," said Mr. Stanford, smiling, as the last of the children arrived.

"What a job!" sighed Bessie, panting, for she wasn't used to such a hard way of going to school.

"I kept thinking I was going to fall over and sink in the snow," said Ned.

"Now you see how important it is to follow in Father's footsteps," said Mr. Stanford.

"Yes," said Ned and Bessie together.

"And that is just how we should follow the Lord Jesus," Mr. Stanford went on. "He has gone before all of us and marked out a way. We must follow Him, putting our feet just where His feet trod. If we go off on our own, trying to find a short cut, we'll lose the way to heaven."

"That reminds me of the memory verse we had the other day," said Ned. " 'Christ also suffered for you, leaving you an example, that you should follow his steps' " (1 Peter 2:21, R.S.V.).

"That's exactly right," said Mr. Stanford. "And now I'm sure you will never forget it."

"I'm sure we never will," replied the children, as the school door opened and the teacher called them in.

◄ Painting by Vernon Nye © by Review and Herald

What fun it was to follow step by step in Daddy's footprints as he led the way to school through the deep snow!

The Light on Their Faces

ALL THE CHILDREN were down with measles—that is, all except Edward. Big Brother had them; so had two younger brothers and two sisters. With five children sick you can imagine that home was like a hospital.

At first nobody was very worried. It was only measles. The children would soon get better and forget all about it.

Then one night William, the eldest boy, took a turn for the worse. Mother noticed it first. She called Father. They did everything they could for the boy, but in vain. Hour by hour he became more feverish. Obviously he was very ill indeed.

"We'd better call the doctor," said Mother.

"I think so too," said Father. "I don't like the look of things at all."

"Better hurry," urged Mother.

There was no telephone in the house in those long-ago days, certainly not on this isolated farm in Wisconsin. So Father sent a messenger with a team of horses to get the doctor, praying that he would not come too late.

The night wore on, but no one slept. All were too worried about William. Those who were not in bed walked on tiptoe.

The children talked in whispers. From the sad look on the faces of Mother and Father they feared the worst. "Do you think William is going to die?" they asked one another.

Edward, not allowed in the room where William was lying, worried most of all. He loved his big brother dearly and was sorry he was so sick. He wanted to go in and talk to him.

He was sorry for his parents, too. He had never seen them so solemn before. They looked so tired, so anxious, so much older.

By and by the clatter of hoofs was heard in the distance. The team of horses was returning. Was the doctor with them? Thank God, he was.

As Mother and Father greeted him, their long faces betrayed their deep anxiety. Quickly they led him to William's bedroom. A moment later he was bending over the sick boy, seeking the cause of his trouble. Mother and Father, hands clenched, watched tensely at the doctor's side, waiting impatiently for his report.

Meanwhile Edward, unable to restrain his curiosity,

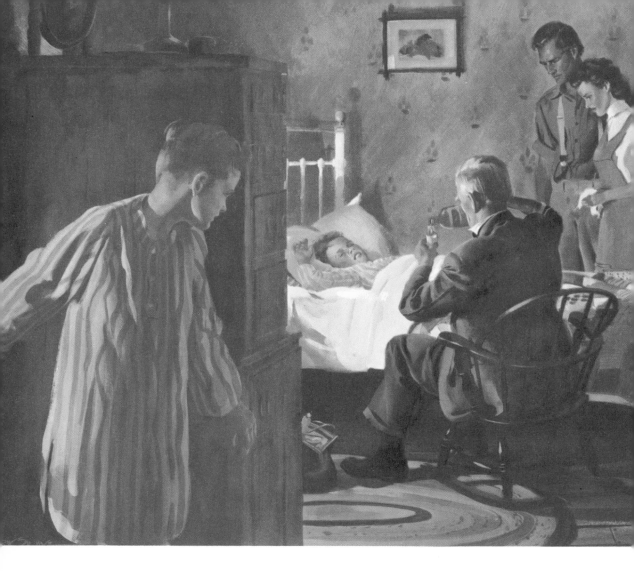

slipped into the room unnoticed and hid behind the big, old-fashioned chest of drawers. From this safe hiding place he was able, unobserved, to see all that went on. What he saw changed his whole life and blessed the world!

Gently and carefully the doctor examined William, feeling his pulse, taking his temperature, listening to his heartbeats, looking into his eyes and ears. Then, having poured out some medicine that was to be given to him later, he

turned to Mother and Father and said,
"Have no fear. He is going to get well."

At this something happened that was beautiful to behold. Instantly the two tired, drawn, anxious faces lighted up with joy and hope, like the sun bursting through clouds after a thunderstorm, or a sudden dawn after a long, dark night.

Never had Edward seen his parents so happy, so relieved. As he watched them a great resolve came into his young heart.

Like most boys of his age, he had wondered what he would be when he grew up. A farmer, perhaps, like his dad; maybe a cowboy, an engine driver, or a prospector for gold. But not now. No. He would be a doctor. Not to make money. Not for any selfish reason, but only that he might relieve pain and worry, and bring light to people's faces!

Years passed by, but Edward never forgot the vision he had seen that night or the high purpose that had then come into his heart. As a medical student he passed through many hard times; but when tempted to give up the struggle, he remembered the light on his parents' faces, and kept on toward his goal.

At last he became a doctor himself, and began to help people as his brother had been helped years before. Soon he too began to see drawn, anxious faces light up as he brought healing to the sick and dying, and new hope to many a troubled heart. His dream was coming true! But he was not sat-

▲ Painting by Vernon Nye © by Review and Herald

isfied. He wanted to help still more people; he wanted to see yet more sad faces light up with joy and courage. So he studied germs that cause disease, and at last became a famous bacteriologist.

Always one of the happiest of men, Edward (Edward Carl Rosenow) found his greatest happiness in helping others, by making sick people well, giving joy for sorrow, and bringing light out of darkness.

Perhaps you have been wondering what you would like to be when you grow up. If you have, and if you would taste life's greatest joy, do something to help the needy and cheer the discouraged. Nothing is so satisfying as doing good to others; no reward so great as bringing light to their faces.

Russ Harlan

11

A Cry in the Night

NOWADAYS WE ARE all familiar with radio and television and all sorts of strange things that nobody had heard of a few years ago. Almost every home has a radio. And what a wonderful thing it is that these little instruments can bring the sound of people's voices to us from hundreds of miles away!

Most of the programs we listen to come from big broadcasting stations in various parts of the country, but occasionally one can hear messages from ships at sea. The dot-dash messages that one hears may possibly be one ship talking to another in Morse code. People who understand this code sometimes can learn what one captain is saying to another.

Many years ago there was a man on the seacoast who made it his hobby to listen to these messages from ships. Long after the big broadcasting stations had closed down for the night, he would go on listening, picking up one ship after another.

Then one stormy night his antenna was blown down. He might have left it down and gone to bed. But no, he was so keen about his hobby that he went out in the dark, climbed

53

◀ Dr. Rosenow in his laboratory. Painted from
a photograph.

the fir tree at the end of his garden, fixed up the wire as best he could, and went back to his radio again.

Hardly had he begun to tune in when he became aware of the repeated call of S O S, the signal of a ship in distress. This, he thought, was interesting indeed, and well worth the trouble he had taken to fix his antenna. The call continued, S O S—S O S—S O S.

Suddenly it dawned upon him that the call was not being

Painting by Harry Baerg

56 answered. Of course, he told himself, that was why it was being repeated so many times. Could it be, then, that he was the only one listening to this cry for help?

Just then, in broken English came this urgent and piteous appeal:

"Please, everybody come and help."

The man jumped to his feet and ran to the telephone. Ringing up the nearest ship-to-shore station, he asked whether they had heard the call. They had not. He begged them to listen. They agreed. Messages were sent out, asking other ships to stop signaling for a time. At once the cry of the little ship was heard. Immediately help was sent, and the ship was saved.

An hour after telephoning to the radio station the man's antenna was blown down again. It had stayed up just long enough for the signal of distress to be heard!

Strange, wasn't it? Often God works with humble means to carry out His purposes.

This lonely man with his little homemade radio was able to bring help to that storm-tossed ship, while the big station was too busy to hear its cry. So even children, young though they are, may by loving deeds bring help and blessing to sad or suffering people.

H. BAERG

Two Pockets, Please

HERE IS A STORY from China, first told, I believe, some years ago, by a missionary of the China Inland Mission.

Paul was a missionary's child. His father had dedicated his life to bringing the gospel to the Chinese, and his mother —well, she was just as much a missionary as his father was for she devoted all the time she could spare to teaching the women who came to the mission for help.

Both were kept very busy all the time, and many times little Paul was left a good deal on his own.

One day he discovered something new. At least, it was new to him, though I think most little boys make the same discovery sooner or later. In a word, he found that by putting his leg over the banister—you know, the handrail beside the stairs—and letting go, he could slide down at quite a good speed without hurting himself. Having done it once, he liked it so much he thought he would do it again. And again. And again.

Of course, he never gave a thought to the effect of each slide on the legs of his brown pants, but you can almost

guess what his mother found when he got undressed that evening. In certain rather important places there were the biggest holes you could imagine. Mother was shocked.

"Oh, Paul, dear," she said, "you make so much extra work when Mamma is so busy! You might have thought about me. I really haven't time to make you another pair."

"I'm so sorry, Mamma," said Paul repentantly. "It was so nice sliding down, and I never thought it would make such holes in my pants."

Mamma forgave him, of course, and soon afterward Paul knelt down to say his prayers. He thanked God for the happy day he had had, for his good home and nice things to eat. Then he prayed for the poor people in China and that God would help Daddy and Mamma tell them about Jesus. At last he remembered the most important thing he wanted to say. For a moment he hesitated.

"Then, Jesus, about my pants," he went on. "I am sorry I wore them out, 'cos Mamma's so busy. You know she hasn't time to make me a new pair, poor Mamma, but You can send me some new ones, can't You, Jesus? And, please, when You send them, I would like two pockets in them 'stead of one."

His little prayer over, Paul jumped into bed perfectly happy, quite sure that the new pants would come from somewhere, and with two pockets in them as well.

Mamma said nothing. She knew we can always count on Jesus to supply what we need, but she also knew that we can't expect that He will always give us just the thing we

She went downstairs to clear up everything for the night. In a corner was a package that had arrived earlier in the day, when she had had no time to open it. She guessed that it had come from some good friends of the mission. She was right.

Cutting the string and spreading out the brown paper, she was delighted to find that it contained clothes of all descriptions, made by loving hands at home. Some were just what she needed for herself. Others would be useful in all sorts of ways on the mission.

Suddenly she saw something that gave her quite a shock. At the bottom of the pile was a pair of brown pants, exactly like the pair Paul had spoiled that very afternoon! Joyfully she seized them and took a closer look. Two pockets!

She ran upstairs, her heart overflowing with happiness and gratitude. But, alas, little Paul was fast asleep. All she could do was to leave the pants hanging over the end of his bed so that he would see them first thing in the morning.

Morning came, and Paul's waking eyes fell upon the new pants. "Mamma!" he cried. "Jesus has sent my pants already!"

Mamma rushed into the room. Paul was feeling the pants all over. He was anxious about one point—the pockets. Had Jesus remembered about them?

He had. There were two pockets!

That package, by the way, had been three months on its journey. Strange, wasn't it, that it should arrive just in time to answer a little boy's prayer?

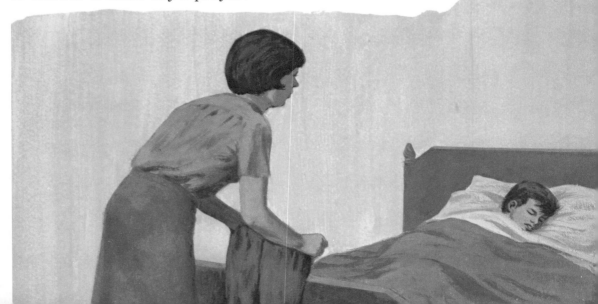

They Set
the Table

MANY YEARS AGO I told in a church service a story about an answered prayer. After the meeting an elderly man came to me and said that he and his family had had a similar experience long ago, when his children were small.

"I remember it," he said, "just as if it had happened yesterday. We had had a very bad winter, and with one trouble after another we had spent our last penny. As for food, there wasn't anything left in the cupboard at all; not a bite.

"The worst of it was when the children came in from play, expecting their dinner as usual. Mother and I didn't know what to say to them. Until then we had always been able to find something or other for them, but now we had come to the end. It was terribly hard to tell them that the cupboard was empty."

"Why didn't you tell somebody in the church about your need?" I asked.

"We didn't like to," he replied. "Nobody does when he gets down and out like that."

"I understand," I said. "And what did you do?"

"Well," he went on, "I called the children to me, and we

talked it all over together. They said, 'Why don't you ask Jesus to send us some food? You talk about His supplying every need and giving us "richly all things to enjoy," and you tell us that the Bible says He will not see "the righteous forsaken, nor his seed begging bread," so why not tell Him all about it, and see whether He will come to our help?'"

"And did you ask Him?" I inquired.

"We did," he replied. "I can see us all now, kneeling around that table. But before we did so, my little girl spoke up.

"'Daddy,' she said, 'don't you think we ought to do all we can to show Jesus we really believe He will answer our prayer and send us food?'

"We all wondered what she meant, and I said to her, 'What more can we do, dear? Jesus can see the cupboard really is empty, can't He?'

" 'Oh, yes,' she answered, 'but don't you think that if we were to set the table and put out the plates and the knives and forks, He would see that we *truly* believe He will send us something to eat at once?'

"We smiled, but I thought, I must not have less faith than this little child. So we put on the tablecloth and began bringing out the dishes and putting the knives and forks in their places. When the table was all set, we knelt down beside it.

"That was a wonderful prayer meeting. I remember how my little girl prayed. 'Dear Jesus,' she said, 'You see we have set the table to show You that we believe You are going to help us. Please send us some food to put in the empty dishes.' "

"And what happened?" I asked eagerly.

"It was wonderful," my friend replied. "So wonderful that I don't suppose you will believe it. But we had hardly gotten off our knees when there was a knock at the door. I went to open it, and there stood two ladies, each carrying a basketful of all kinds of food. They were practically strangers to us, but they said they had been impressed to bring us something to eat. We invited them in and showed them the table we had set and told them how we had scarcely finished praying when they arrived. Really, I don't know who were happier, they or we."

"I think I know who must have been the happiest of all," I suggested, "and that was the little girl."

"I believe she was," he said, "for it seemed to her that Jesus had actually sent two angels from heaven to answer her prayer."

14

Reggie's Idea

"THESE ARE HARD TIMES," said Mother, "and I'm afraid there will be no money for Christmas presents this year."

"Oh, you've said that every year," said Bessie.

"But I mean it this time," said Mother. "We simply can't afford it. I'm sorry, but that's the truth."

The children looked very gloomy. Reggie and Bessie went out into the back yard to talk it over.

"I don't mind so much," said Reggie, "although I was looking forward to getting some new tires for my bicycle. What I don't like is that little May and Flo will be disappointed. They count on getting something so much. They will cry their poor little eyes out."

"Whatever happens," said Bessie, "we must see that they get something. I don't mind if I don't get those new books I wanted, so long as the darlings get something to please them."

Both Reggie and Bessie loved their baby sisters very much indeed, and always did everything they could to make them happy. So you can guess they could not bear the their stockings empty.

"Suppose there isn't any money to spend," said Reggie bravely, "that doesn't stop our making something for them. I've got a bright idea."

"What is it? Do tell me," said Bessie.

"I'll tell you," said Reggie. "Let's make them a fine doll-house. They will just scream with joy at it. I can make the house and put in the doors and windows, and you can make the curtains and stick the paper on the walls."

"What a great idea!" said Bessie. "That won't cost us a penny. Let's begin right away."

"Come on, then," said Reggie, leading the way to the storage shed.

"Ah, here's a nice box," he said. "Look, the sides are all nice and smooth, and it's just the right shape. All I have to do is to build a roof, put a door on, and divide the inside into rooms."

"How lovely," said Bessie. "I almost wish you were going to make it for me. Won't they both be happy!"

So Reggie began to work at once. He had learned a little

about using tools at school, so he knew just what to do. Very soon his wooden box was looking like a house, with a nice, pointed roof. He cut two windows in each side, and made a door and four windows in the front. Of course he made the whole front to open on hinges, so that one could get at all the rooms easily. Then he painted the sides red and lined them with pencil to make them look like bricks. The top he painted gray to look like slates.

It took him a few days to finish his part of the job, and then Bessie began. In the meantime she had found some rolls of wallpaper up in the attic, from which she cut enough to cover the walls of the house. Then she had found some old pieces of cloth that made fine curtains, and other pieces of thick material that did for rich-looking carpets on the floors. By the time her nimble fingers had finished, the inside of the house looked really pretty. But it was bare of furniture.

So Reggie got busy again. Out of some empty matchboxes he made a chest of drawers, with drawers that really opened and closed. A piece of polished tin, cut into an oval shape with Mother's old scissors, did for a mirror. A square piece of wood and four legs soon made a table, and it did not take a great while to make some chairs to match it. Before long, indeed, Reggie had the house furnished from top to bottom, and it really did look nice. When it was all done, they shut the big storage shed door and waited for Christmas morning.

◀ Painting by Manning de V. Lee

Reggie and Bessie worked for a long time making the little dollhouse look as real as possible, with paint, wallpaper, and furniture.

68 It came at last. Very early, while the two little girls were still sleeping, Reggie and Bessie brought in the beautiful dollhouse and placed it on the foot of their bed. As they were doing so, one of them accidentally kicked the iron bedpost, and—up jumped little May.

She rubbed her eyes in astonishment and shouted, "Oh!" That woke little Flo, who promptly sat up in bed and yelled with delight.

"What a beautiful house," they cried. "Is it Bessie's?"

"No, it's for you—both of you," said Bessie. "Reggie and I made it for you. Why, don't you know, this is Christmas Day,

and this is the beautiful surprise we have been saving for you!"

"Oh, how lovely!" cried the little girls together as they jumped out of bed and threw their arms first around Bessie's neck and then around Reggie's.

As for Reggie and Bessie, the joy of that moment more than made up for all the trouble they had taken in making the house, and in their happiness they quite forgot that Santa Claus had passed them by.

They had discovered the truth of that saying of Jesus: "It is more blessed to give than to receive."

Talking Drums

MORE THAN A THOUSAND years before any-one had heard of radio, black people in Africa were able to speak to one another over long distances by means of talking drums.

I don't mean that they had drums that could speak as you and I speak; yet they talked just the same!

You see, in every village men were trained to play the drums so skillfully that messages could be sent by the sound that the drums made.

Some of the drums were so large that their sound would travel as far as twenty miles or more. And as soon as the drums would begin to sound in one village, the drummer in the next village would pick up the message and begin to sound it out on his drum. So from village to village the word would go until the whole countryside had heard it.

When really big things happened, the news would be sent in this way all across the whole great continent.

It is said that when Queen Victoria died, and the news was cabled to West Africa from England, Africans living hundreds of miles from railway and telegraph lines immedi-   71

◄ Painting by Kreigh Collins

The great talking drums of Africa boom out their messages from village to village clear across the continent.

72   ately began talking of the death of the "Great White Queen."
They heard the news even before government officials, by
means of the talking drums.

The largest drums are made from huge, hollowed-out tree
trunks. Sometimes these measure as much as twelve feet
long and five feet wide. Think of a drum that size! No wonder the sound of it carries twenty miles!

Wouldn't you like to hear drums like this being played?

Someone who has heard them all his life has said: "Shud-
dering down the wind come their voices. . . . Boom-tap-boom!
Dumm . . . dum . . . t-rat . . . t-t-r-r-rat! Bo-o-o-o-om!"

You can almost hear them, can't you? I wonder what they
are saying? Perhaps some awful disaster has happened, a
flood, or a fire, or some great chief has died.

The drums are still talking today though now replaced in
many parts of Africa by telegraph, telephone, and radio.

But I am thinking of other drums. We might call them
God's drums. And they are talking very loudly, bringing
news, not only of things that have happened, but of things
that are going to happen.

Boom! Boom! Boom!

Yes, all the terrible things that are happening in the
world today, all the suffering of so many people, all the sor-

rows of so many fathers and mothers and little children, all
the crime and cruelty, all the little wars and big wars, are shouting a message to us.

Boom! Boom! Boom!

"Wake up!" they say to us. "Wake up! Be on the watch for something that is coming soon!"

Jesus knew all about these things, and He told us that there would be "talking drums" in these days; only He called them by a different name. " 'There will be *signs,' "* He said, " 'in sun and moon and stars, and upon the earth distress of nations in perplexity at the roaring of the sea and the waves, men fainting with fear and with foreboding of what is coming on the world; for the powers of the heavens will be shaken' " (Luke 21:25, 26, R.S.V.).

In the last days of earth's history, said Jesus, everything would talk to us—the sun, the moon, the stars, the sea, the people, the heavens, and the earth. Talking drums thundering out the news of His coming!

And He added, " 'When these things begin to take place, look up and raise your heads, because your redemption is drawing near' " (verse 28, R.S.V.).

"I will come again," said Jesus, bringing a great and wonderful hope to all mankind. Then He was crucified.

Six weeks later the call was sounded anew by two angels who said to the disciples, " 'This Jesus . . . will come in the same way as you saw him go into heaven' " (Acts 1:11, R.S.V.).

It was sounded again by the apostle Paul who said, "The Lord himself shall descend from heaven" (1 Thessalonians 4:16).

Peter declared, "The day of the Lord will come" (2 Peter 3:10).

And John repeated the message: "Behold, he is coming with the clouds, and every eye will see him" (Revelation 1:7, R.S.V.).

As the years and the centuries passed, the message of hope was sounded by thousands of other lips as Christians spread the tidings from nation to nation that their Master would someday return as King of kings and Lord of lords. From the crucifixion till today this witness has never ceased.

But today the drums are sounding everywhere—the signs in all the earth that "Jesus is coming again!"

And wherever the message is heard—in churches or homes or along the busy streets—it does something wonderful in people's hearts. It cheers them up. It drives away their fears and sadness. It sets them aglow with the certainty that soon the night of sorrow and suffering will end in the dawn of eternal day.

And if we can hear them and their message, what shall we do about it?

Shall we not look up into His face and say to Him, "Jesus, I'm glad that You are coming again. I am so eager to see You. I want to live in the beautiful land of peace You are preparing for those who love You. I love You too. And I want to be ready to meet You when You come. Please make me ready. Take all sin out of my heart. Help me to be good today and every day until You come again."

Won't you say that? And say it now?

If you do, there will be no doubt about what will happen in that great day, for we are told that " 'he will send out his angels with a loud trumpet call, and they will gather his elect' " (Matthew 24:31, R.S.V.)—those who belong to Him, from Africa and America and Europe and Asia and the whole world.

That means that they will be looking for you! The angels looking for you! How very wonderful! And they will find you. I know they will. And they will take us all home to that beautiful land where there will be no more war and "no more death, neither sorrow, nor crying, neither shall there be any more pain" (Revelation 21:4).

◄ Painting by Vernon Nye © by Review and Herald

Many boys and girls all over the world are looking forward to the day when Jesus will fulfill the promise "I will come again."

How Grandma Came for Christmas

AT LAST THE DAY HAD COME to open the money boxes! How long it had taken to fill them! What hard work it had meant, what careful saving, what giving up of candy and nice ribbons and special treats! To Hilda and Mona it had seemed as though they would *never* be allowed to open them, and sometimes they had even said it wasn't worthwhile putting the money in.

But at last the day had come! It was a week before Christmas, and of course everybody was wanting all the money he could find for presents and new dresses and things. How glad the children were that they had heeded their mother and had kept the boxes unopened till now! Mother was right, after all.

Click! went the key in Mona's little cash box, and there inside she saw the pile of pennies, nickels, dimes, quarters, and one half dollar. What joy! She counted it all up, and Hilda counted it afterward, just to make sure it was right. Four dollars and fifty-one cents! What a lot of money for a little girl!

"Now you open yours," said Mona. "I wonder who has the most?"

Hilda's was a strange-looking money box, and it certainly
held money tightly. It was such a job to get it out. She had to
use a knife, but as she poked it in, out came the pennies,
nickels, dimes, quarters, and two half dollars. It was a lovely
sight.

"Oh!" said Mona, "you have more than I!"

"It looks like it," said Hilda. "Let's count it up. One, two,
three. Why, I believe there's more than five dollars!"

And so there was. It came to $5.28. How happy they were!
Never had they had so much money to spend all at once.

Then came the big question. What should they spend it
on? Soon they realized how little they had really saved.

There were so many things they wanted to buy, and most
of them cost more than they had saved.

Mona thought she would like to get a pretty dress, but
how far would $4.51 go? Hilda's first thought was for a beau-

tiful handbag, the kind with two pockets in the middle and a mirror. But again, how far would $5.28 go? Then they talked of other things they would like—so many things—but try as they would they could not stretch their money nearly far enough to cover all their desires.

"I'm getting tired of trying to decide," said Hilda. "This money is a bother."

"Do you know," said Mona, "I wonder whether the trouble is that we are trying to spend it all on ourselves?"

Hilda sat very quiet and still. "Perhaps it is," she said.

"Just for fun," said Mona, "let's try to think how we could spend it on some other people."

"Mom, for instance," said Hilda.

"Yes, or even Grandma," said Mona.

" All right. You write down what you would buy for them and I'll do the same."

So they both found pencil and paper and began to write. Hilda soon made a long list—long enough to use up her $5.28 many times over.

"You don't seem to have put down much, Mona," she said, looking at her paper.

"No," said Mona, "but I've got an idea! I've thought of something that would be a beautiful present for both Mom and Grandma."

"Come on, then, let's have it," said Hilda.

"Well," said Mona, "you know how Mom has been longing to have Grandma come down here to stay with her for a while? Well, the only reason Grandma doesn't come is that she can't afford the fare and Mom can't afford to sent it to her. Wouldn't it be wonderful if we were to send Grandma her fare ourselves, and invite her down to surprise Mom?"

"Mona, you are a genius!" said Hilda. "I should enjoy that much more than a new handbag. Let's do it right now."

"Isn't it just lovely?" said Mona. "I'm so glad you like the idea. I'd much rather see Mom happy than have a new dress.

Let's get a pen and some writing paper. You'll write the letter, won't you?"

"All right," said Hilda. "You tell me what to say."

So together they wrote to Grandma:

"OUR DEAR GRANDMA,

"We all want you very much to come down here for
Christmas. Mona and I have been saving up for a long time to
pay your fare, and you will find it in this letter. Don't lose it,
and be sure to come soon. We shall expect you next week.

"With lots of love from HILDA and MONA."

"Oh, Mona," said Hilda when she had finished writing;
"whatever will Mom say when Grandma comes?"

"Oh, that's part of the fun. She'll be so pleased and surprised she won't know what to do with herself."

Picking up their money and putting on their coats, the
two went down to the post office, bought a postal money
order for $9, and mailed it to Grandma. Chuckling all over

and enjoying their secret immensely, they returned home to await the big surprise.

For the next few days the girls could not settle down to anything. Every footstep made them jump, and every creak of the front gate gave them a start. They felt inside themselves that they had done something big and beautiful, not unmixed with mischief, and they just couldn't keep still.

Every now and then they would burst out laughing, for no apparent reason whatever.

Mother wondered what could have gone wrong with them. They often had innocent little secrets they tried to keep from her, but this was rather mysterious.

Then at last came a different knock at the door.

"Hilda, there's someone at the door," called Mother. "Go and see who it is."

But Hilda guessed that the great moment had come, and she wanted Mother to have the surprise they had planned so long. Making up a hurried excuse, she said, "Do please go yourself, Mom."

So Mother hurried to the door, rather hot and bothered— thinking it was the postman or the milkman. She opened the door sharply—and there stood Grandma, with her handbags and trunk, as though she had come to stay a month.

"Well, well!" cried Mother. "Whoever—whatever! Isn't this wonderful! But how did you come? Who could have dreamed you would be here for Christmas!"

"Why, didn't you expect me?" said Grandma, equally surprised.

There was a loud chuckle in the background.

"Ah, those two young scamps," said Grandma. "I guess they are at the bottom of this."

Then came the explanations, and everybody was happy.

After the excitement had died down, Grandma called the children to her and, slowly and mysteriously, opened her trunk.

◄ Painting by Manning de V. Lee

Mamma hurried to the door, rather hot and bothered. She opened the door sharply—and there stood Grandma with her handbags and trunk.

"I'm not too old to use my fingers yet," she said, pulling out a couple of packages. "Here's a little dress I've been making for Mona, and I've got a wee handbag made all of beads for Hilda."

"Oh, no!" cried the girls together, looking at each other in amazement.

"Why, don't you want them?" asked Grandma.

"Want them! I should say we do! They are just perfect," said Hilda. "But how did you know? They are the very things we were going to buy for ourselves with the money we had saved in our boxes."

"Well, did you ever!" exclaimed Grandma. "Do you know, girls," she said, "I believe the good old Book is right when it says, 'He that hath pity upon the poor lendeth unto the Lord; and that which he hath given will he pay him again.'"

17

Mike, the Blacksmith's Son

MIKE WAS ONLY a blacksmith's son, but he lived to bless the world and give to all mankind the secret of a great new power.

Mike was born in London, England, in 1791, a few years after thirteen British colonies in America had become the United States of America. In those days there were no cars, no telephones, no radios, no TV's, not a single electric light, or motor, or anything electrical in all the world.

Then came little Mike to change things for everybody.

As a boy he played around his father's forge, no doubt working the big bellows that made the fire white hot. Day after day he watched his father hammering the heated iron on the anvil, making horseshoes and metal rims for wooden coach wheels.

Mike was a thin and hungry boy. His family was poor. Often there was not enough to eat. Because all the money his father earned had to be used for food and clothing, there was none left for Mike's education. At thirteen he left school and went to work. No high school for him, or university degrees.

Fortunately Mike was apprenticed to a bookbinder. More

fortunate still, he longed for knowledge, and loved to read.
All sorts of books came to the bindery to be bound, and Mike
read as many of them as he could, especially the scientific
books. Some of these were about chemistry, others about
electricity. He enjoyed them more than any storybook. By
and by he began to do some of the experiments mentioned in
these books. Then he went on to try some new ones he
thought out by himself. He began to see that there were all
sorts of possibilities in electricity that even the great scientists of his day had not thought about yet. How he longed to
know more about these things! If only he could go to school
and learn about them from a teacher!

One day a customer, who knew of Mike's interest in
science, asked him whether he would like to go and listen to a
lecture by the famous scientist, Sir Humphry Davy. Mike did
not need a second invitation.

That night was a turning point in the boy's life. He took
full notes of everything the great scientist said. These he
copied carefully and bound in a beautiful leather binding,
which he sent to Sir Humphry with a letter telling of his deep
interest in science.

Some time later, on December 24, 1812, there was a knock
on his door, announcing Sir Humphry Davy's coachman, with
a note from his master asking Mike to call to see him next
day.

Talk of a "shot heard round the world"! That was a *knock* heard round the world, a knock that has echoed down the years, knocking, as it were, on the doors of millions upon millions of homes in every land on earth.

Mike left the bookbindery and went to work for the great scientist at a wage of twenty-five shillings a week (at that time worth a little more than five dollars). But he didn't care about wages; he loved his job. He was happy beyond words. He could hardly believe his good fortune.

Eagerly he watched Sir Humphry carry out his experiments, keeping careful note of everything he did. So pleased was the scientist with his new assistant that he took him

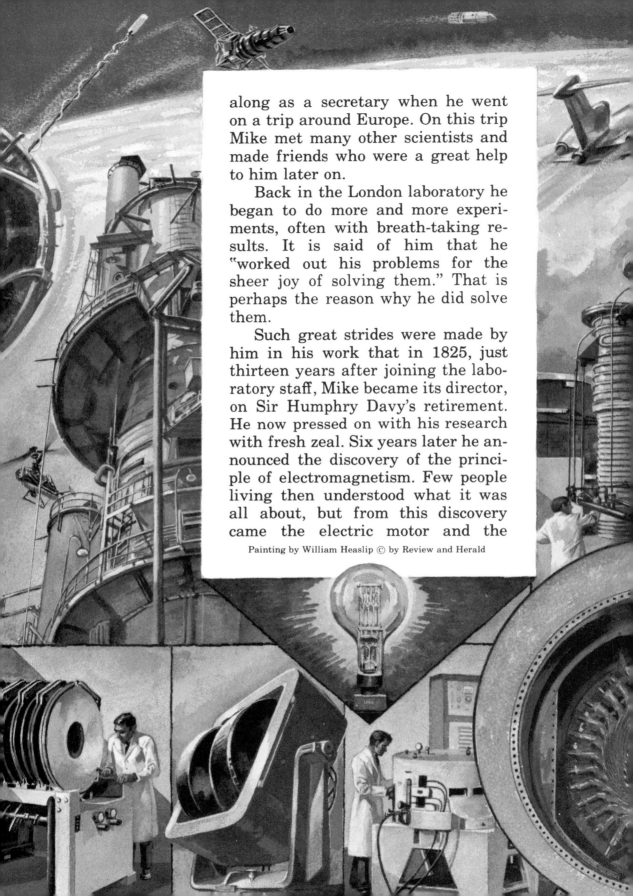

along as a secretary when he went on a trip around Europe. On this trip Mike met many other scientists and made friends who were a great help to him later on.

Back in the London laboratory he began to do more and more experiments, often with breath-taking results. It is said of him that he "worked out his problems for the sheer joy of solving them." That is perhaps the reason why he did solve them.

Such great strides were made by him in his work that in 1825, just thirteen years after joining the laboratory staff, Mike became its director, on Sir Humphry Davy's retirement. He now pressed on with his research with fresh zeal. Six years later he announced the discovery of the principle of electromagnetism. Few people living then understood what it was all about, but from this discovery came the electric motor and the

Painting by William Heaslip © by Review and Herald

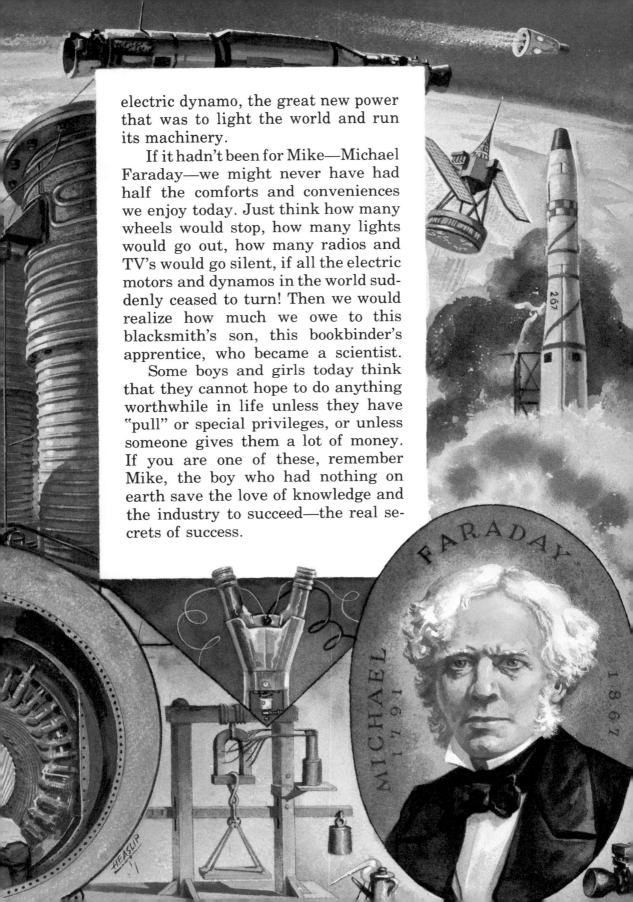

electric dynamo, the great new power that was to light the world and run its machinery.

If it hadn't been for Mike—Michael Faraday—we might never have had half the comforts and conveniences we enjoy today. Just think how many wheels would stop, how many lights would go out, how many radios and TV's would go silent, if all the electric motors and dynamos in the world suddenly ceased to turn! Then we would realize how much we owe to this blacksmith's son, this bookbinder's apprentice, who became a scientist.

Some boys and girls today think that they cannot hope to do anything worthwhile in life unless they have "pull" or special privileges, or unless someone gives them a lot of money. If you are one of these, remember Mike, the boy who had nothing on earth save the love of knowledge and the industry to succeed—the real secrets of success.

MICHAEL 1791 FARADAY 1867

Faithful Jock

ONE LOVELY summer day I saw a dog in a most unexpected place. I'm going to call him Jock, for, though I tried hard, I never found out his real name, but it really doesn't matter.

I was traveling on a train that was climbing up steep mountain slopes, round and round, twisting and turning up and up, several thousand feet above the sea.

And then, suddenly I saw a dog running toward the tracks. I looked out of the window to make sure. Yes, there he was, a fine black retriever, running at top speed beside the train!

Where did he live? Why was he there? Did he want the train to stop and take him on board?

Then an interesting thing happened. From the very last coach a newspaper was thrown out by somebody. Instantly the dog stopped, turned, and dashed after it, as if eager to learn the latest news of the outside world.

A porter came to the window where I was standing, and as we watched the fast-receding form of the dog, I asked whether he knew anything about him.

◄ Painting by Arlo Greer

Every day faithful Jock ran beside the train, then stopped and dashed after the newspaper that was thrown out to him from the last coach.

"Yes," said the porter, "that is the most faithful dog I have ever known. He belongs to a man who lives in that little shack over yonder, and for years now, winter and summer, he has met this train to pick up his master's paper. Winter or summer, he never fails, and we expect him here as regularly as the sunrise."

"But how about the winter snows, when you have to run a snowplow in front of the train?" I asked.

"It makes no difference to him. Snow or rain or hail, he is always here on time. In fact, if he weren't, we'd wonder what had happened."

Faithful Jock! Bless his dear old courageous heart!

Do you wonder that I leaned out of the window once more to catch one last glimpse of his shining black coat as he disappeared down the bank in the dusk.

Geoffrey's Bandsmen

IT HAPPENED ON THE WAY BACK from a band concert. I mean the quarrel happened then.

As a special treat, Geoffrey and his sister Anne had been taken to hear the band one evening.

They loved going to hear the band, and would promise their daddy that they would be good as angels for weeks, if only he would take them there.

Of course, as soon as the music was over they usually forgot all about their promises.

Well, the concert was over one night, and Daddy, Geoffrey, and Anne had begun to walk home. Unfortunately, both children wanted to hold Daddy's right hand. A very silly thing, of course, for surely Daddy's left hand was just as comfortable to hold as his right hand. But then most quarrels begin over very silly little things.

"I was there first," said Geoffrey.

"No, you weren't; I was," said Anne.

"I was; you get away," said Geoffrey.

"I was; you get away," retorted Anne.

"What does it matter?" asked Daddy.   91

"I had your right hand first," said Geoffrey.

"No; I did," said Anne. "Anyway, it's my turn."

"No, it isn't."

"It is."

"It isn't."

"Stop it, children!" cried Daddy. "What will people think of you both, making all this fuss at this time of night?"

"It's my place," said Geoffrey, taking no notice, and trying still harder to push Anne away.

"It isn't yours; it's mine," cried Anne, holding on to Daddy's hand still more tightly.

"Will you stop it, Geoffrey?" said Daddy firmly. "Come round and take my other hand at once."

"Don't want to," said Geoffrey sulkily, suddenly dropping behind. "I'll walk by myself then."

"All right," replied Daddy. "But next band night things will be different."

So the procession moved toward home, with Geoffrey dropping farther and farther behind, and shuffling his feet along in a manner that must have made the angels weep.

It was long past bedtime when they reached home. Mamma hurried the children up to bed without making too many inquiries as to what had happened.

Geoffrey was soon between the sheets, and it was not long before he dropped off into a troubled slumber.

Oh my! What was this? He was at the band concert again. Surely it could not be! But he was. And to his utter amazement, he was the conductor. Behind him were hundreds of people, many of whom he recognized. Lots of boys from his school were there too. He felt very proud of himself. Imagine being the conductor of the band in front of all his school friends. My! wouldn't they all like to be in his shoes? He made up his mind that he would make their ears tingle with the wonderful music he would bring from the band that night.

Then he looked around at his bandsmen. Yes, they were all there. Were they ready to play? Yes. He tapped his baton smartly on the music holder, and swelled up with pride. But nobody moved.

He tapped again. No one seemed to take the least notice.

"Start!" he shouted. "Can't you hear me? Start!"

At this the drummer banged his drum and the man with the trombone blew one great long note. The people behind him laughed. He could hear his school friends tittering.

"Play!" he cried again. "Start! All of you start!"

He tapped furiously on the music holder.

The man with the piccolo blew a piercing blast and stopped. Then the cornets began, but they all seemed to be playing different tunes. Geoffrey was in despair. He waved his arms in an endeavor to beat time, but there was no time. Rather, there were all sorts of time. The clarinets had begun now, all on different notes. Geoffrey shouted to them to look

at their music, but they took no notice. Now all the rest of the players began, and the confusion became terrible. It seemed as though each one was playing a tune of his own. No one took any notice of anybody but himself. Geoffrey could hear "Three Blind Mice" and "Home Sweet Home'" and "Old Man River" all mixed up together. Every man was playing just what he liked and how he liked and in any time he liked.

As for Geoffrey, the players took no notice of him whatever. He might as well not have been there. And yet he felt that he was responsible. The people behind him were expecting great things of him. And this was all he could do! It was terrible. As the din increased, Geoffrey became frantic.

"Stop!" he shrieked at them all. "Stop! Stop it, I say! Can't you hear me? Do what you're told, will you! Oh, why don't you listen to me? Stop! Stop, I say! Stop!"

"There, there," said Mamma, putting her hand on his

head. "It's all right, dear; don't worry anymore."

Geoffrey sat bolt upright in bed.

"So I'm not at the band concert, after all," he said.

"At the concert?" laughed Daddy. "You're right here in bed."

"Oh!" said Geoffrey. "You should have heard them. They just wouldn't do what I told them, Daddy. They were so obstinate. They just played their own tunes as loud as they could, and wouldn't take a bit of notice when I shouted at them."

"Who?" asked Daddy.

"The bandsmen, of course. Didn't you hear the noise?"

"Well, no, I can't say that I did," said Daddy. "I heard a noise, and I also saw someone acting like that on the way back from the concert tonight."

"Oh—er—yes," said Geoffrey, waking up fully at last. "I wonder whether that's why I dreamed that dreadful dream."

"I should think it was," said Daddy.

"Well, of all things," said Geoffrey as he dropped back on his pillow and went to sleep.

Geoffrey's dream was not forgotten in the morning, and Daddy found it very useful later on when the old trouble began to come back again.

For whenever Geoffrey showed any signs of grumpiness or disobedience after that, all Daddy had to say was, "How about your bandsmen, Geoffrey?"

It always had a wonderful effect!

Doreen's Jewel Box

JUST ONE MORE WEEK, and it would be Doreen's birthday. To think of it! She would be ten years old. Mother said she was just "five minutes to ten." Doreen was not at all backward in saying out loud what she was expecting.

"You see, Mother," she would say, "I've been too big for a tricycle for a long time. I need a bicycle."

Later: "Mother, don't you think I should have a big doll house with stairs and a fireplace and electric lights?"

Mother listened patiently, explaining that she and Daddy had barely enough to buy food and clothes for the family.

But Doreen didn't seem to hear. "You know, Mother," she went on, "when I'm ten I'd like a pretty jewel case."

"A jewel case! What an idea! You don't wear jewelry."

"Well, Kitty Naylor has one. Can't I have anything nice?"

"Oh, don't say that," said Mother. "I wouldn't be surprised if something would turn up yet to make you happy."

"A bicycle?" cried Doreen eagerly.

"I don't think it could be that," said Mother. "It would cost too much. But, let me see, if you are very eager for a jewel

97

◀ Painting by Vernon Nye

Doreen reminded her mother that there was just one more week before her birthday.

box, that gives me an idea—a different idea."

"Oh," exclaimed Doreen. "What kind of idea?"

"Well, we'll see," said Mother with a mysterious smile. When her birthday came, it was still hardly light when she awoke, pushed down the covers, sat up, rubbed her eyes, and looked around. There was no bicycle and no doll house. On the chair beside her bed lay a flat package.

Jumping up, Doreen put on her clothes, with one eye all the time on the package. She had decided to keep the pleasure of opening it until she went downstairs.

There was no bicycle or doll house downstairs. Evidently Mother had spent all her money on this gift.

Snip! snip! went the scissors, and off fell the string and then the paper. Inside was a beautiful cardboard box of a mottled-green color. "How pretty!" she exclaimed, carefully lifting the lid. She peeped inside. "A Bible!"

"Yes," said Mother. "You will find that it is a very special jewel box, packed full of the richest gems."

Doreen looked doubtful. "Gems?"

"Yes, memory gems." said Mother. "Daddy and I have spent lots of money on this jewel box, and if you are careful, it will last all your life. When you are grown up you will still be telling about the lovely gems you found in this jewel box."

Doreen carefully lifted the Book out of its box. "Look at the gold edges with the red shining through! And what thin paper and lovely leather! It's just like a jewel box, anyway."

Inside, on the first blank page, Doreen read: "To our darling Doreen on her tenth birthday, with love from Mother and Daddy." Below was a verse of Scripture: "Acquaint now thyself with him, . . . and lay up his words in thine heart" (Job 22:21, 22).

Doreen read it. "Is that the first jewel?"

Mother smiled. "Yes. Now why not look for pearls? And diamonds, sapphires, rubies, emeralds, and other precious stones."

◄ Painting by Vernon Nye © by Review and Herald

Doreen held her Bible close and recalled the beautiful verses, "Acquaint now thyself with him. . . . And lay up his words in thine heart" (Job 22:21, 22).

Remember now thy Creator in the days of thy youth.

Eccl. 12:1

"But how can I find them?" asked Doreen.

"Keep on the lookout for beautiful sentences beginning with *P.* They will do for pearls. Those beginning with *R* will do for rubies, *E* for emeralds, and *D* for diamonds. See?"

"Yes," said Doreen, "what a lovely idea!"

"I can think of a pearl," said Mother, "in the fourth chapter of First John, verse 18. 'Perfect love casteth out fear.'"

"I know one," said Doreen. "'Praise ye the Lord!'"

"That's right," said Mother. "There's a whole string of those pearls in Psalms 148 to 150."

Doreen turned the thin leaves carefully. "Yes," she cried, "I can see two, three, four pearls all at once!"

"Yes," said Mother. "Don't you think that this is the best sort of jewel box? Ordinary pearls and diamonds would sparkle in their box, but we'd have to shut them up and put them away. But these jewels from this wonderful Book we can carry with us all day long, and they become more and more beautiful."

"Yes, Mother," said Doreen, "they sort of go on sparkling in our heads afterward, don't they? Where are some rubies?"

"A verse that begins with an *R*—What about 'Re—mem—'"

"I know," cried Doreen. "'Remember the sabbath day, to keep it holy'" (Exodus 20:8).

Mother agreed. "And can you think of an emerald, a text beginning with an *E?* Remember the one about good gifts?"

"Oh, yes—'Every good gift and every perfect gift is from above, and cometh down from the Father'" (James 1:17).

"Yes. Now try to find a diamond and a ruby in Psalm 37, verse 4."

"Here's the diamond," said Doreen. "'Delight thyself also in the Lord; and he shall give thee the desires of thine heart.' And the ruby: 'Rest in the Lord, and wait patiently for him' (verse 7). What does that mean?"

"That Jesus doesn't want us to worry," said Mother, "if we don't get all that we think we need right away. We are to leave it with Him to give us what is best for us."

"Does that include bicycles and doll houses too, Mother?"

"Maybe. Jesus will see that we get what we ask for just as soon as He sees it will be good for us, or He will make sure that we get something better. We can trust Him. That is what it means to 'rest in the Lord, and wait patiently for him.'"

"Now, add a sapphire, a message from Jesus Himself. It's in the last chapter of the Bible, the next-to-last verse."

Doreen soon found it. "'Surely I come quickly.'"

"Read the emerald in the same verse," said Mother.

"'Even so, come, Lord Jesus,'" read Doreen. "Mother, this *is* a wonderful jewel box."

"Yes," said Mother. "It's the world's richest treasure chest."

◄ Painting by Peter J. Rennings © by Review and Herald

Jesus and His beautiful angels have been busy preparing a place for us. Soon He will come to take us there to live with Him forever.

Reunited
by an Onion

IN THE EARLY DAYS of American history, when the Western States were being developed, some of the hardest-working people were ministers of the gospel. These were the circuit riders, who rode on horseback from one community to another, preaching and conducting baptisms, marriages, and funerals. Sometimes they would be away from home for months at a time, enduring all sorts of hardships and riding thousands of miles a year.

Mr. Matthews was one of these brave and busy circuit riders. He had a huge parish, covering hundreds of miles in every direction, which constantly called for all his time and attention. With these heavy duties and his large family of

twelve children, he was sometimes a very tired man.

Coming home one day after a long absence, he found that his son Jack had failed to complete some work that he had been told to do. Heated words were spoken, and it was not long before Jack was suffering from the effects of a severe spanking. Father simply would not put up with disobedience.

Now Jack was a high-spirited boy, and nothing wounded his pride so much as being spanked, especially when he felt that he did not deserve it. This time he was so angry that he decided to run away.

His favorite sister, Elsie, who was about his own age, pleaded with him not to go, but he would not listen to her. She begged him to let everything rest for a few days, but nothing moved him. He was determined to go.

Next morning, without saying good-by to anyone but Elsie, Jack went away, determined never to return to his father's house.

Now it was Elsie's turn to be cross. She, of course, sided with Jack, and said it was her father's fault that he had gone away. Therefore she would have nothing to do with her father, or with his religion.

Every day she became more and more bitter. She would hardly speak to either of her parents and positively refused to take any part in family worship. She would neither read the Bible nor say her prayers, and in her heart she secretly resolved that she would never be a Christian, never!

Meanwhile no word came back from Jack. He had vanished completely out of the home. Elsie felt that the joy of life had gone away with him, and her heart became hard as steel. Then one morning, while preparing the dinner, Mother discovered that she needed just one more onion, and Elsie was the only daughter near at hand to send.

"Elsie!" called Mother. "I do so need just one more onion to finish this potpie. I wish you would go and get me one."

"Where are they?" asked Elsie coldly.

"In the barn, on the second floor," said Mother. "Mind how you go up the ladder, dear. And you might as well bring me two or three extra ones while you are about it."

Elsie went without a word, or even a smile. She had long since ceased to smile around the house and was secretly longing for the day when she, too, could run away. Then she would go and find Jack.

Going over to the barn, she climbed the ladder to the second floor, and, looking around, soon saw where the onions had been laid out for winter use. She picked up half a dozen and was walking back to the ladder when she heard a noise below.

Footsteps! Someone was coming stealthily toward the ladder.

Who could it be?

Holding her breath, she listened and guessed that it must be her father, the very last person on earth she wished to meet at that particular moment. Suddenly all the hatred she had been fostering in her heart overflowed. She did not want to speak to him, no, nor to look at him. She never would again, never!

But what could she do?

Looking around quickly, she spied an old, unused door leaning against the wall. It was the only possible shelter; so on tiptoe she ran swiftly toward it and was barely hidden when she heard her father coming up the last section of the ladder.

Holding her breath for fear he would find her, she waited anxiously, hoping he would go down again immediately when he found the loft empty. But he did not go down. Instead Elsie heard a strange sound as of something falling gently on the floor, and she held her hands together in fright.

After a few moments of suspense she heard her father talking out loud. Had two people come up into the loft? No. He was praying!

Painting by Wm. Hutchinson ▶

Cramped behind that door, Elsie listened to the most wonderful prayer she had ever heard; she couldn't run away from it. She just had to stay and hear every word.

Father was praying for his family. For every child, from the oldest to the youngest, for Elsie herself, and especially for Jack. When he reached Jack he broke down completely, sobbing as if his heart would break; asking God to forgive him for being so angry with Jack as to drive him away from home; praying that even now God would move upon Jack's heart by His Spirit and bring him back.

Elsie was stunned. She could hardly believe her ears.

So Father did love Jack after all! And wanted him home again! And was so very, very sorry he had been angry with him!

More than that, he was willing to pray for Elsie, too! Elsie, who had been so rude to him, so cruel to him all these many weeks since Jack had left. She knew she had not prayed for Father like that.

Suddenly she felt she could not stand it a moment longer. She must run from the scene, or her heart would break.

Elsie rose and slipped from behind the door. As she did so, she caught sight of Father kneeling on the floor, wiping the tears from his eyes.

She gave in.

"Father, I'm sorry," she said, putting her arms around his neck and bursting into tears.

"So are we all, Elsie," he said. And everything was all right again from that moment.

Meanwhile, Mother was beginning to fuss about the missing onion, wondering why Elsie had been so long getting it. But when she saw Father and daughter coming across the yard with arms around each other, faces tear-stained but radiant, she suddenly understood and ran out to meet them, the onion and the pie all forgotten.

That night, believe it or not, Jack returned.

(In later years, by the way, Jack himself became a minister, and Elsie a minister's wife.)

22

Tommy's Trucks

TOMMY WAS ONLY a very little boy, but he had a will of his own. That is, he liked to have his own way, and he didn't like to do what he was told.

Now, Tommy had some beautiful little trucks and cars, toy ones, of course, that Daddy had bought for him from time to time. He must have had a dozen trucks at least, and as for the cars, well, there were blue cars and orange cars and green cars and yellow cars. Some were racers and some were nice little compacts. There was an ambulance too, and a fire truck, which was Tommy's special delight.

Tommy loved to play with all his precious trucks and cars on the front porch, though sometimes he would take them out to the driveway that led to the garage. He would make "roads" for them in the gravel and imagine that they were real.

Of course, Tommy was supposed to bring them indoors every evening after he had finished playing, but that was something he never wanted to do. He would say that it didn't matter; that he would bring them in later; that it would be all right to leave them out all night ready for him to play with in the morning.

One afternoon he made up his mind that he wouldn't
bring them in. "No," he said, "I'll bring them in after a while.
I'm not ready yet."

"But, Tommy," urged Mother, "something may happen to
them out there. They might be stolen; a car might run over
them."

"They'll be all right," said Tommy. "Nothing has happened to them so far."

"But you'd be very sorry if something did," said Mother.
"You know you would."

"I'll bring them in after supper."

"It'll be dark then. Bring them in now."

"Later on."

"I said now, Tommy."

"All right."

But Tommy didn't bring them in. He went to the front
door and then forgot all about them.

By and by, after dark, two big headlights came flashing
up the drive. It was Daddy coming home.

"Oh, look out for my trucks and cars!" shouted Tommy.

Alas, it was too late.

Crunch! Crunch! Crunch!

Daddy's big car had run over them all.

The ambulance was flat as a pancake; the fire truck was
completely wrecked; the racing cars would never race again.

"Oh, look what you've done! Look what you've done!" cried
Tommy rushing outside, shining a flashlight over all his ru-
ined toys and sorrowfully picking them up, one by one.

"I'm sorry," said Daddy. "I'm dreadfully sorry."

"You don't need to be," said Mother. "Tommy was told to
bring them in long ago."

"Oh, my poor cars!" wailed Tommy. "Oh, my poor fire
truck! Why did you run over them?"

"You should know why," said Mother. "Remember how
many times I spoke to you about them?"

◄ Painting by Jack White

**Tommy loved to play with his precious trucks
and cars on the driveway.**

114 "I forgot," cried Tommy, "and now they're all smashed up. There isn't one whole one left. Oh, what'll I do?"

It was a sad procession that went indoors.

"I suppose," whispered Daddy to Mother, "I'll have to go downtown again right now."

"Not yet," whispered Mother. "Let us wait and see whether he has learned his lesson."

They did not have to wait long.

Tommy had learned his lesson all right. Indeed he decided to pick up his toys when Mother said to, *just when she said it.*

Perhaps I should add that, all in good time, Daddy and Tommy *did* go on a little trip downtown together, Tommy looking very happy and excited on the front seat of Daddy's car.

Can you guess what they brought back with them?

STORY **23**

"Daredevils"

"DO YOU KNOW WHAT I can do now?" cried Maurice, running indoors excitedly.

"I can't guess," said Mother, "but you are always up to something."

"Well, at last I can ride my bicycle without putting my hands on the handle bars."

"That may be very clever," said Mother, "but I'm afraid it's not very sensible."

"Why not?" asked Maurice, rather crestfallen. "All the boys try to do it, and I can do it now better than any of them."

"Maybe you can," said Mother, "but what is the purpose of it?"

"Aw, I don't know," said Maurice; "it's lots of fun."

"I suppose it must be," said Mother, "but isn't it rather risky?"

"Risky? Oh, you're always talking about things being risky," said Maurice, rather annoyed.

"Of course, we all have to take risks sometimes," said Mother, "but why take unnecessary risks?"

"There's no risk in that," said Maurice. "It's easy." 115

"Well, I don't like your doing it," said Mother, "especially with so much traffic on the roads today. After all, what are handle bars for, if not to be used to steady yourself?"

"Oh!" exclaimed Maurice, "don't worry so, Mother; it's all right."

With this he bounded out of the house, closing the door, I am sorry to say, with a much louder bang than usual.

A moment later he was on his bicycle again, gliding down the hill from his home, his arms folded in front of him and his face indicating supreme indifference to all his mother's caution.

Gathering speed, he glided along in great style, glancing from side to side to see whether anyone might be looking at him.

Near the bottom of the hill Maurice spied two girls standing at the roadside, and consequently sat up a little straighter, folded his arms a little more confidently, and tilted his chin just a little bit higher. He was not "showing off," of course. Oh, dear no! Just letting the little girls see how fast a boy could ride down a hill without holding the handle bars; that's all.

What Maurice failed to see, however, was a brick lying in the road, right in the path of his bicycle. If his chin had not been tilted so high, if he had not been sitting up so very straight, if he had not had his arms folded, he would have seen it easily, and everything would have been different; but he didn't see it, and a moment later he felt a terrific bump. The front wheel twisted, the handle bars swung around, and before Maurice had time to think what was happening, he had crashed into the ditch at the side of the road.

Some men working near, hearing the noise, ran to see what had happened, and found Maurice rolling in mud, with his bicycle all bent and broken on top of him.

What a pickle he was in! Slimy water dripped from his clothes as they dragged him out, while his face, hands, and knees were red with blood from cuts and scratches.

The men were very kind and helped Maurice up the hill again to his home, one of them carrying the wrecked bike

over his shoulder.

"Oh, dear!" cried Mother, her eyes wide with alarm, as she opened the door and looked out on the strange procession. "Whatever has happened?"

Yet she hardly needed to ask. She guessed. It was, in fact, just what she had been expecting for some time.

"My poor boy!" she said, leading Maurice indoors and beginning to clean him up. "It's a wonder you weren't killed."

She changed his clothes and washed his wounds, binding them up till he looked as if he had just come back from a war.

Then with Maurice at last comfortably—that is, more or less comfortably—seated by the fire, she reminded him of the little chat they had had less than an hour before.

"It is right to take risks in a good cause," she added, "such as helping people in distress, but to take risks just to gratify our vanity is very foolish. There are always people—provided others are looking on—who are ready to go and peer over the edge of a precipice; or stand on the end of a pier when the

waves are dashing over and the wind is blowing hard; or
drive their cars at breakneck speed; or swim in the ocean
beyond their depth; but these are not the truly brave people.
Such actions are a form of pride, not of courage. They are an
effort to call attention to themselves, and so are really just
cheap, showy, self-advertisement."

"But what has that to do with me?" asked Maurice.

"Everything," said Mother. "For a moment you were just
the same as these people I have mentioned, a daredevil, and
the accident that sooner or later comes to all daredevils came
to you."

"Um," said Maurice. "All the same it's rather nice to ride
a bike without having your hands on the handle bars."

"Maybe it is," said Mother, "but I don't think it's worthwhile, do you?"

Maurice mournfully surveyed his bandages.

"I don't believe it is, after all," he said.

24

Boisterous Bimbo

IT WAS HALF-PAST FOUR in the afternoon. All was quiet and peaceful in the Cooper household. Connie, already home from school, had seated herself comfortably in a chair by the fire to do her homework. Baby Sister was on the hearthrug, building a castle with her bricks and humming softly and happily to herself.

Suddenly they looked up. They had heard a familiar and unwelcome sound.

"La-la-la-la-la-la-la——"

"Bimbo!" said Connie. "Now we'll have no peace."

She was right. A moment later the back door was opened violently and banged against the kitchen wall.

"Hi!" cried 8-year-old Bimbo. "Where's everybody? Yippeee!"

He burst into the dining room, flinging the door back against the sideboard with such a crash that a small vase clattered to the floor and smashed.

"Bimbo, you naughty boy!" cried Connie. "Whatever will Mom say?"

120   "Hi, Con. I couldn't help it. What are you doing here any-

way? You don't want to read any more today, do you? Come
and play marbles."

With that Bimbo emptied his pockets on the table, marbles by the dozen dropping on the floor and rolling in every
direction.

"I don't want to play marbles today," said Connie. "I've
got to learn this poetry for tomorrow morning."

"Aw, come on," cried Bimbo, "drop that. You can do it
later." And so saying he knocked Connie's book out of her
hand.

Connie jumped out of her chair in anger.

"What do you mean by that?" she cried. "Why can't you
leave people alone?"

"Oh, stuck-up, are you?" teased Bimbo, pulling Connie's
hair and kicking her book across the room. Unfortunately it
hit Baby Sister's castle and brought it tumbling down in
ruins.

"Boo-hoo-hoo!" cried Baby Sister. "You horrid Bimbo!
You've broken my castle, and I wanted Mamma to see it. Boo-
hoo-hoo!"

So saying, she picked up a brick and hurled it as hard as she could at Bimbo's head. He ducked, and it missed him, striking a picture on the opposite wall and shattering the glass.

At this moment the back door opened again and in walked their mother.

"What does this mean?" she asked, looking around at the angry, tearful faces and the litter of broken glass and china on the floor. "I heard the noise when I was halfway across the yard. Why, the room looks like a battlefield!"

"Wasn't my fault," said Bimbo; "they just don't seem to like me; that's what. I didn't do anything."

"Mom, it was all his fault," said Connie heatedly. "We were both so peaceful and happy till he came in. I wish he would never come home from school again."

"And he knocked my castle over," added Baby Sister. "Horrid Bimbo!"

Mom understood. "You come with me, Bimbo," she said. "I think we must have a little talk together about this."

Bimbo followed his mother upstairs. Mom found a little strap that she kept for such occasions in her room. Then Bimbo began to sing in a different key.

Afterward Mom began to talk with him.

"Bimbo," she said, "you must pull yourself together and behave more like a civilized boy. You are so wild and rowdy that one would think you belonged to a tribe of savages. Every day you seem to get worse. You are always upsetting the others and making yourself a nuisance."

"I didn't mean to," said Bimbo.

"Of course you didn't," said Mom, "but if you would only make up your mind to be different, you could be. And you must. Things cannot go on like this. You really should be ashamed that Connie and Baby Sister seem to dread the very thought of your coming into the house!"

"Oh dear!" sighed Bimbo.

"I have an idea," said Mom. "I want you to make up your mind that as soon as you come into the house each evening, you will say something nice and kind to everybody, and think how you can help make the others happy."

"Ugh!" sighed Bimbo.

"You will, won't you?" urged Mom.

"I'll think about it," said Bimbo.

And at that Mom left him.

Bimbo did think about it. Indeed, he thought a lot about it. But school came the next day, and he forgot. At least, he forgot until he turned the corner of his street on the way

124   home. Then he remembered; and all the way up the street he laid his plans as to what he would do when he got indoors.

Creeping up to the back door, he entered so quietly that nobody heard him. Tiptoeing across the room, he surprised Connie almost out of her wits by dangling a bag of candy under her nose.

"I didn't eat all my candy today," he said, "and I brought this home for you and Baby Sister."

"Huh?" gasped Connie, too taken aback to know what else to say.

Bimbo, a little self-conscious, ran quickly out into the kitchen again, shut the door softly, and seeing some dirty dishes in the sink began to wash them.

He was in the middle of drying them when Mom came in.

"Well!" she cried, dropping down upon the nearest chair and holding her hands in the air. "Did you ever! My wild, boisterous Bimbo is tame at last!"

Bimbo heard—and smiled, and always after that—at least almost always—when he turned the corner of the street on his way home from school, he would begin to plan some pleasant surprise for the others.

Soon, instead of Connie and Baby Sister saying, "Oh dear, there's Bimbo coming!" they began to say, "Hurrah! Bimbo will soon be home!"

25

One Good Turn

"GOOD-BY, RONNY."

"Good-by, Mother."

"Be a good boy at school today; don't forget."

"I won't," shouted Ronny as he dashed out the gate and down the road.

As he disappeared Mother went into the house again, her face clouding over a little.

"I do wish Ronny would be a better boy," she said to herself. "He is so very selfish. He always wants everything for himself, and it's so hard to get him to do anything for anyone else. I wonder what I can do to make him different?"

That afternoon, just after dinner, Ronny joined in a baseball game in the field near the school. It was a fast, rough game, with lots of good pitching and hard hitting. At last it came Ronny's turn to bat.

There was nothing he loved so much as a game of ball, and to hold a bat in his hand was the height of happiness. Proudly he walked to the plate. Carefully he watched the first ball, and with one mighty hit sent it right over to the wall of the playground, but it was a foul.

125

The next ball came across. Flushed with his first effort, he swung again, fully intending this time to send the ball clear over the wall into the street, and so make a name for himself the boys would never forget.

But suddenly something went wrong. Ronny could never tell just what it was. He thought he swung too quick and was hit by the ball. What Ronny did know was that he suddenly felt a sharp pain in his forehead.

As he put up his hand he felt something wet and sticky. He turned very pale and dropped the bat.

"I'm afraid I'll have to go in," he said, turning toward the school.

The boys crowded around and helped him to a chair in one of the classrooms.

"I'll be all right," he said to the others; "you go on with the game." With that they left him.

But Ronny did not feel all right. He felt very sick. He wished with all his heart that he were at home, and that Mother would come and bathe his forehead.

Just then one of the senior boys looked into the room.

"Hello, what's the matter?" he asked in a kind voice. "Hurt yourself?"

"A little," said Ronny, trying to look brave. "Ball hit me on the forehead."

"That's too bad. Better come along with me. I'll bathe it for you if you'll let me."

"Thanks," said Ronny. "It is looking pretty bad, isn't it?"

"Oh, we'll soon have it all right," said the senior boy.

"This isn't so bad as having your head knocked off, is it?"

"No," said Ronny, smiling despite the pain.

They went into the rest-room and there, with a tenderness equaled only by Mother herself, the senior boy bathed the wound and put on antiseptic from the school first-aid kit. Then with a jolly laugh he bade Ronny good-by and rushed off to his next class.

When Ronny reached home that night he had a great story to tell.

"Wasn't he nice!" he exclaimed. "You know, Mother, I'd never spoken to him before. I can't understand why he should have been so kind to a stranger. And he is one of the big boys, you know."

"It was good of him, indeed," said Mother. "I appreciate it ever so much. You will tell him so, won't you? It was a kind thing to do. I hope you will always be as thoughtful as he was, Ronny."

"Oh, I couldn't be as good as that," sighed Ronny.

Two days passed. Again it was evening. Ronny was due home at half-past four. But he did not come. Five o'clock passed, and still no Ronny. Mother began to get angry. Then she grew anxious.

At half-past five, when Mother was just about to telephone the police station, Ronny turned up.

Mother was waiting for him on the doorstep.

"Ronny," she said severely, "what do you mean by coming home at this hour? Don't you know how late it is? I really can't allow——"

"It's all right, Mother. I—I—I had to walk home."

"Walk home!" said Mother in astonishment. "Walk home, indeed! Didn't you have your money for the bus fare? I know I gave it to you this morning before you left."

"I know, Mother," said Ronny, a twinkle coming into his eye. "You gave me the money all right, but I gave it away to one of the boys."

"Gave it away!" cried Mother, more astonished still.
"What for?"

"I just couldn't help it," said Ronny. "You see, I—er—I met one of the little boys—you know, out of the baby class, we call it—just as I was going to get on the bus. He looked very pale and sick, so I asked him what was the matter. He said he didn't feel well enough to walk home, and he had lost his money. So, well, there was nothing else to do. I—er—well—I just gave him mine and walked instead. And here I am."

Mother threw her arms around Ronny's neck and dropped some tears down the back of his new sweater.

"Why, what's the matter, Mother? It's nothing like what that big boy did for me the other day."

"Oh Ronny," said Mother, smiling through her tears, "it's just everything to me."

STORY **26**

Attacked by Bandits

LISTEN! WHAT WAS THAT noise that broke the desert stillness?

The lonely traveler looked around sharply. A stone had rolled down the hillside and fallen beside him.

He was a little nervous, for this part of the road between Jerusalem and Jericho was known to be the hiding place of bandits. On one side the ground dropped away; on the other, it rose steeply. All over the hillside were great rocks behind

which robbers could wait for passers-by.

"Perhaps it was nothing," said the traveler to himself, again urging his donkey forward in the hope of reaching Jericho before nightfall. But he did not get far.

Suddenly from behind the boulders leaped a band of savage-looking men, waving sticks and knives and shouting to him to stop.

Goading his donkey, the traveler made a desperate attempt to escape, but all in vain. In a moment the robbers were upon him, beating him with their sticks and stabbing him with their knives until he fell to the ground bleeding and unconscious.

As he lay there half dead, the robbers stripped off his clothes and, taking all his valuables and his donkey, hurried off into the hills.

Naked, bruised, and bleeding, the poor man lay there on the road for hours. As consciousness returned he felt the awful pain of his wounds but was too weak to call for help.

After a while he heard footsteps. At last someone was coming! The person drew nearer, and the wounded traveler

noticed that he was a priest. How thankful he felt! Surely the
priest would help him.

But no. That selfish priest just looked across the road at
the poor suffering man, and then walked away from him as
fast as he could go, afraid, probably, that the robbers might
catch him, too. Wasn't that mean of him?

As the sound of the priest's footsteps gradually died away,
the poor wounded man lost hope. He felt he could not live
much longer.

But hark! More footsteps. Yes! They were drawing nearer.
Surely this person would help him.

It was a Levite, a man who helped in the Temple services
up at Jerusalem, and one who should have been the first to
assist anyone in need. He came across the road and looked
down upon the poor, naked sufferer. Then, what do you suppose he did? Like the priest, he just left him lying there and
hurried away! Why? Perhaps because he didn't like the task
of binding up the poor man's wounds, or because he didn't
want to spend the time to take him home. Perhaps he was in
a hurry. But wasn't it the meanest thing he could have

done? I wonder how he would have liked to be left lying naked and wounded on the hard roadway?

Again the footsteps died away, and again the hopes of the sufferer sank. Would no one help him? Every minute seemed an hour.

"What was that?"

Clippety-clop, clippety-clop!

It was surely someone coming on a donkey. Would he stop?

Again hope revived in the poor man's heart, but then, as the rider came into sight, he recognized him as an enemy— one of the Samaritans, who were known to hate the Jews. It was too bad! Would no one help him?

But see! the Samaritan has stopped! He has noticed the poor man lying beside the roadway. He has jumped off his donkey and is coming toward him. Apparently he doesn't take any notice of the fact that the man is a Jew but just sees someone needing help.

"Poor fellow!" said the Samaritan, as he stood over the injured traveler. "Can I help you?"

Opening one of the saddlebags he had on his donkey, this good Samaritan took out some pieces of cloth and some ointment, and bound up the poor man's wounds. Then he gave him something to drink, and wrapped him in some of his own clothes. Helping him carefully to his feet, the Samaritan

gently lifted the sufferer onto his donkey. Slowly they made their way toward the inn, which stood on the road between Jerusalem and Jericho. The Samaritan walked all the way, guiding the donkey with one hand and supporting the wounded man with the other.

When they arrived at the inn, the Samaritan called the
innkeeper and told him what had happened. Then he arranged for the wounded man to be put to bed and kept at the inn till he should be better. As the sick man had been robbed of all his money, the Samaritan told the innkeeper that he would pay the whole bill. Then he said good-by to the sick man, and went on his way. Wasn't he a good, kind man?

But the best of it was that when this Samaritan did this kind deed, he had no idea that anyone would ever hear about it. He just did it because he believed it was the right thing to do, even though it was an enemy who had been hurt. But the innkeeper did not keep the story to himself. He told others, and Jesus heard of it.

Jesus was so pleased that He repeated the story in one of His talks, telling His hearers that that was just the way He wanted them to treat their enemies.

Jesus wants us to remember the story of the good Samaritan, and always be kind to those in need, doing unto others as we would like them to do unto us.

Just
Twenty Minutes

SOMETHING VERY WONDERFUL happened
to a friend of mine not long ago. This man had a large family
and needed a great deal of money to keep everything going
week by week.

Sometimes he wondered how he would make ends meet;
but always, just when things looked darkest, a light would
shine through. His great faith in Jesus was always rewarded.

There came a time when he badly needed sixty dollars for
taxes—not very much to a wealthy man, but a huge sum to
this poor farmer.

And he had to have it by the next Monday morning.

Over and over he thought of his problem. How could he
get sixty dollars by Monday morning? It seemed impossible.

He thought of his cows. Yes. He would be willing to sell
one of them to raise the money, but nobody was buying cows

at this time. In fact, no cow buyer had been to his farm for months. There seemed no way out.

What could he do?

In his heart he believed that the dear Lord whom he loved would do something for him. But how or when?

Sunday morning came, the last day before he had to pay the taxes. He rose, as usual, at three o'clock and went out to the dairy to milk the cows.

Returning just before six, he decided to take a brief nap to refresh himself for the rest of the day's tasks. Before doing so, however, he reminded the Lord that this was the day he needed that sixty dollars.

At six o'clock he lay down, and in a few moments was fast asleep. But he didn't sleep long.

Bang, bang, bang!

Someone was knocking on the window.

Startled, my farmer friend awoke, jumped from his bed, and demanded to know what was the matter. For the moment he was too dazed to know how long he had slept, but supposed

it must now be eight o'clock at least.

"Sorry to disturb you," said his farm helper, "but there's a man here who wants to speak to you."

"About what?"

"He wants to buy a cow."

The farmer was at the door in a moment, his heart beating fiercely with excitement that he dared not show. Would the Lord now prove His providential care?

Outside he found a man who lived several miles from his farm and whom he had seen occasionally before.

"Sorry to bother you so early," said the man, "but I'm needing one more cow to complete a carload. Spent all yesterday searching for one in vain. Then I thought of you. Do you have one to sell?"

"It so happens that I do," said the farmer. "Come and look at it."

They went to the barn.

"How much do you want for it?" asked the visitor.

"Well," said the farmer hesitatingly, "I hardly know what to say. I don't know what the market price is today, but I do know that I badly need sixty dollars for it."

Without a word the visitor took out his checkbook, wrote a check for sixty dollars, and prepared to depart with the cow.

"By the way," said the farmer, "when did you think about coming to see me about a cow?"

"This morning," said the visitor. "At six o'clock I was strongly impressed that you would have a cow to sell me, and that I should come and see you. So I got into my car and drove straight here."

"What is the time now?" asked the farmer.

"Six-twenty."

"Only six-twenty!" exclaimed the farmer. "Amazing! Perfectly amazing."

It was. It had taken just twenty minutes for his prayer to be answered.

STORY **28**

Ben's Loyalty

AT THE END OF THE LAWN, where it merged into the wild patch of trees and bushes, stood Margie's playhouse. Her father had made it for her, and she was never so happy as when she could be in it all alone with Ben.

Ben, of course, was her dog—a beautiful shepherd dog, who was devoted to his five-year-old mistress. They played so happily together, Ben watching all the time to see that no harm came to Margie.

Then one day, as Margie was walking through the garden to the playhouse, she heard a strange rattling noise. She could not remember having heard anything like it before, and she looked around, wondering what it could be. Then she walked on, but a moment later the same rattling noise came again, only louder and nearer this time.

Then something happened.

All of a sudden Ben, who had been walking nearby, flashed across in front of Margie, and in a moment a terrific fight had begun.

Terrified, Margie rushed back to the house.

"Mommy, Mommy!" she cried. "Ben's in a fight. Come quick, come quick!"

Mother hurried out and soon saw what was the matter. Ben had his teeth in a rattlesnake. Over and over they rolled. It was terrible to watch.

Just then Father came on the scene with a hoe in his hand and began hacking at the snake as best he could. At last the battle was over and the snake lay dead.

Then Father took Ben in his arms and began to look him over. He found three bites, two on his mouth, one on his head.

"He can look after those on his mouth," he said, "but I'm afraid of the other one. He can't lick that."

Gallant Ben, exhausted, lay down, licking away at the wounds on his mouth. Soon his head began to swell, and it got bigger and bigger until it didn't look like a dog's head at all.

Father came back to look at him, Margie, weeping and very frightened, at his side.

"Will he get better, Daddy?" she asked.

Father looked Ben over again.

"There's not much hope. Unless Jesus does something special for your pet, Margie, and very soon, I'm afraid we shall have to say good-by to him."

Margie ran indoors, and kneeling beside her bed, poured
out her little heart to God.

"O dear Jesus," she pleaded, "my dear Ben was so brave looking after me, and the naughty snake bit him, and now he's so very, very sick. Daddy says he's going to die if You don't do something quick. So please do something quick as You can, for I can't spare him. Please, Jesus, do."

By and by Margie went back to see Ben, taking some fresh water for him to drink. She found him still alive and the swelling definitely smaller.

"Come, Daddy!" she cried, running into the house. "Ben's getting better. He really is. Come and see." Father went out to see the dog and could hardly believe his eyes. Ben was indeed better, and within a week or so he had fully recovered.

Margie told me that through all the years since this happened, she has never doubted that Jesus answered her prayer.

I think He did too, don't you?

STORY **29**

Saved From
an Earthquake

HERE IS A TRUE STORY of the wonderful
way Jesus cares for His children in the midst of the worst dis-
asters. It happened at the time of an earthquake.

On the outskirts of the city was a little church, and just
beyond it the home of the pastor and his family. Father was
the minister, and Mother, well, she was almost everything
else, including the organist.

Now, because they were both so busy at the church, they
usually left their little baby girl at home during services. She
must have been a very, very good baby, because she slept
peacefully in her baby carriage until Father and Mother
came home.

On the morning of the earthquake, however, Baby would
not sleep. She was restless and disturbed, and nothing would
quiet her. As the time for meeting approached, poor Father
and Mother found themselves in a most awkward fix, and
didn't know what to do. For Father had to preach the sermon
and Mother had to play the organ; so what was to be done
with Baby? They couldn't leave her behind crying, and yet
how could they take her to church in such a restless mood?

144

When there was hardly a moment left, they decided to take Baby along and make the best of it.

They did so, and the service went very much as usual until the last hymn had been sung.

Then came the first awful rumble of the approaching earthquake. Everybody rushed outside, just in time to see the building opposite the church crash to the ground. Looking toward the city, they saw buildings toppling over.

Naturally the minister and his wife ran to their own home.

It was still standing, except one wall where the brick chimney had fallen.

Then they saw something that made their faces grow pale. The baby carriage in which the baby would have been sleeping was crushed flat as a pancake, buried beneath the

ruins of the chimney!

Had Baby not been so restless that morning, she would have been killed instantly with the first shock of the earthquake.

Somehow I feel that the angels were watching over that dear baby that day. How anxiously they must have tried to keep her from sleeping! And how glad they must have been when they saw Father and Mother take her away to church!

Jesus does look after His own, doesn't He?

And I know the story is true, for I met that baby the other day, now grown up into a fine, lovely girl. As I looked at her, I wondered what great destiny the Lord has in store for her, seeing He saved her so wonderfully from the earthquake.

We need His protection, too, so let us pray this prayer to Him tonight:

Painting by Russell Harlan ▶

"Jesus, Friend of little children,
    Be a friend to me;
Take my hand and ever keep me
    Close to Thee.

"Step by step, O lead me onward,
    Upward into youth;
Still becoming wiser, stronger,
    In Thy truth.

"Never leave me nor forsake me,
    Ever be my friend;
For I need Thee from life's dawning
    To its end."

From
Slavery
to Fame

IT IS HARD to realize that there were slaves in the United States not much over a hundred years ago. But it's true. And little Booker was one of them.

Born about 1856, he lived in a small log cabin. There was no glass in the windows, and the door was too small for the hole in which it swung on rusty hinges. The cabin had no floor but the earth, and the "storecupboard" for sweet potatoes was a deep hole in the living room, covered with boards. In one of the walls there was also a cathole about seven inches square, to let the cat pass in and out during the night; but as there were lots of other holes in the shack, Booker thought this one seemed unnecessary.

As a little boy he never played. He didn't know what it was to play. He was always cleaning up, running errands, taking water to the men in the fields. And if he didn't do things exactly right, he was cuffed and beaten by those in charge.

Booker was still a small boy when freedom came, following the Civil War. He remembers going to the "Big House"—as the white people's mansion was called—and

hearing somebody read a paper to all the black people who had gathered there. He didn't understand what it was all about, but Mother did, and she kept weeping and saying, "This is the day I have been praying for but fearing I would never see."

Free at last, his mother left the plantation and walked over the mountains into West Virginia and settled in a village called Malden. But freedom did not mean ease. To Booker it meant working in a salt furnace from four in the morning till late in the afternoon.

Of course he did not go to school. There was no school for black boys and girls. So he could not read or write. But he did notice that the boss of the packers would put the number "18" on the barrels of salt which his stepfather filled, and after a while he was able to draw that figure, though he didn't know about any others.

One day there came into his heart a desire to read, and he begged his mother to get him a book. Somehow, though very poor, she managed to buy one. And what do you suppose it was? A children's storybook with pretty pictures? No; but an old, worn copy of Webster's spelling book!

At this time, remember, he could not read; and there was no one to teach him to read. There was not a single black person anywhere near who could read, and he was too afraid of the white people to ask any of them to help him. So all alone he taught himself the alphabet. After a few weeks he found himself reading that spelling book with the same enjoyment you might find in the stories of this book.

About that time another black boy, who had learned to read in a northern State, arrived in the village. As soon as the people found out this boy could read, they arranged to buy a newspaper so that he could read the news to them in the evening. Booker envied him. He wanted to be able to read like this boy from the North.

Not long after this a little school was started, the first for black people in all West Virginia. It had only one teacher but

Painting by Russell Harlan

everybody wanted to go to it. Boys and girls, fathers and mothers, even grandfathers and grandmothers. The old people wanted to learn to read the Bible before they died.

Poor little Booker, however, was not allowed to go. His stepfather said he must stay at work and earn money. So he labored in the salt furnace and watched the other boys and girls going to school.

After a while he persuaded his stepfather to let him attend school, but it was on condition that Booker should work from four A.M. till nine, and return after school for two more hours of work. How would you like that? But Booker did it, so eager was he to learn.

Arriving at school, he ran into an unexpected problem. When asked for his name, he replied, "Booker."

"Booker what?" asked the teacher.

Booker was puzzled. He only had one name, so far as he knew. He had never heard of another. However, if he was supposed to have two, he would invent one. So "Booker

Washington," he said. And that name stuck to him from then till now. He added the "T" later. It stands for Taliaferro, a name his mother liked.

Little by little Booker began to learn. Gradually the ambition grew in his heart to get an education and do something worthwhile with his life. Then his stepfather made him leave school and go to work in a coal mine. It was a bitter disappointment to the boy, for he hated to work underground. It was so dark down there. Sometimes his light would go out, and he would lose himself in the many low, narrow passages. Sometimes there would be explosions, and other boys like himself would be hurt.

Yet it was in this very mine that the idea came to him which altered his whole life. One day he overheard two men talking about a great school for black people which had been opened somewhere in Virginia. He crept nearer so that he could listen better. The men were speaking of the Hampton

sounded like heaven to Booker. He made up his mind that one day he would go there at all costs.

Two years passed, during which he saved every penny he could for the long journey to Hampton. Yet his wages were so little that in two years he did not have nearly enough to travel the five hundred miles to the institute. But he set off at last, going first in the stagecoach, then begging rides in wagons and walking when he couldn't ride. When he reached Richmond, eighty-two miles from Hampton, his little store of money had run out. He had nothing left for food. That night, and several nights after, he slept under the wooden sidewalk of the city street. Fortunately he was able to get a job at the docks. Here he earned enough to buy food and save a little for the last part of his journey.

Finally he arrived at the Hampton Institute, the goal of all his dreams, with exactly fifty cents in his pocket. Fifty

cents to start his education! But it was one step forward.

After his long journey, and having had no bath or change of clothes for a long time, he was so untidy that the head teacher did not want to let him stay. Several hours passed, and he began to wonder if, after coming so far and putting up with so much, he would have to go back, rejected. Then the lady said to him, "The next room needs cleaning. Please sweep it."

This was his chance. He swept that room three times. He took a cloth and dusted it four times. Every bench, table, and desk, all the woodwork around the walls, he dusted again and again till he could find not a speck more to remove. Then he reported to the lady, and she came to inspect what he had done. She looked carefully at everything, even wiping a handkerchief over the table to see if she could pick up any dirt. But there was none. "I guess you will do," she said.

This "entrance examination," Booker said afterward, was the most important he took in all his life. Now he was in a real school at last! True, he had to work very hard, for he had

to earn all his board, room, and tuition expense. But he made
the most of every precious hour that he had for study.

Some things, of course, were new and difficult for him. He was puzzled, for instance, when he found sheets on his bed. He had never seen sheets before, and he wondered what they were for. The first night he slept *under* both of them and the second night *on top* of both of them. But he soon learned what to do.

He learned many other things, too. Most important was the "dignity of labor," as he afterward called it—that to work hard is no disgrace to any boy, but a blessing. Then, too, he learned that life's greatest joys are to be found in helping others. And it was this which led him to give his life to help the less fortunate of his own race.

After graduating, in 1875, he went back to his own home town as a teacher. Not long afterward he was invited to join the faculty of the Hampton Institute, where he had been a student.

When a call came for a principal for a new training school at Tuskegee, Alabama, Booker Washington was recommended. Arriving there, he asked for the school, but was told, "There isn't any, yet."

Undismayed, he replied, "Then we'll build one."

This he did, beginning with a small, leaky building, with only thirty pupils, and expanding it until it became one of the greatest institutions of its kind in the world.

Impressed with the good work Washington was doing for the black boys and girls of the South, many people, rich and poor, sent him money. Andrew Carnegie gave him $600,000 in one sum, and one poor old black woman, over seventy years of age, clad in rags, came to him one day and said, "Mr. Washington, I ain't got no money, but I wants you to take dese six eggs I'se been savin' up and put 'em into eddicatin' our boys and gals." Booker never was quite sure who gave the most, this old woman or Carnegie.

Russ Harlan

Photo courtesy of Tuskegee Institute

Tuskegee Institute was established by Booker T. Washington in a small, leaky building. Today it is one of the greatest institutions of its kind in the world.

In 1973 Tuskegee had a teaching faculty of 300 with 3,171 students, more than 160 buildings, and 5,189 acres of campus.

Booker T. Washington, the slave boy who became founder and head of the Tuskegee Institute, will ever be remembered as one of the truly great men of his time. He sought nothing for himself, but spent his life for others. When Harvard University awarded him a degree, its president called him "a wise helper of his race, good servant of God and country." And that's praise enough for any man.

◄ Painting by Russell Harlan

Booker T. Washington, born in slavery, founder of the famous Tuskegee Institute, was one of the truly great men of his time.

STORY **31**

After Dark

"OH, NORA!" CRIED MOTHER one day as she opened a letter at the breakfast table. "Isn't this wonderful news? Your Aunt Elizabeth is coming to stay with us for a whole week, and she's going to bring Brenda along with her. Won't that be lovely?"

Nora didn't seem to be very pleased.

Mother noticed it.

"Why, dear," she said, "aren't you glad Brenda is coming? It will be so much fun for you to have her to play with you."

"I don't want Brenda to come," said Nora.

"Oh, my dear, why not?" asked Mother, surprised. "My little girl isn't feeling a little selfish again, is she?"

Being the only child in the family, Nora liked to have everything her own way. Mother knew this only too well and had invited Brenda just to help Nora learn the joy of sharing her playthings happily, and to teach her how to get along with other people.

"She'll break my best dolls," said Nora, "and she'll mess up all my toys. I wish she wouldn't come."

158 "Oh, but Nora," said Mother, "you could have such a won-

derful time together if you would give her a friendly welcome and try to be pleasant to her. Then she would be pleasant to you, and both of you would be happy."

"I don't want her to come," repeated Nora. "Anyway, where would she sleep?"

"I thought it would be nice if she slept with you," said Mother. "After all, she is your cousin, and——"

"I won't have her in my bed," snapped Nora, stamping her little foot. "Why, she would take up all the room and I never would be comfortable a single minute. Anyway, she might kick me."

"Oh, but she's not as big as that," smiled Mother. "After all, dear, you have a very big bed for a little girl. There's plenty of room for two."

"No, there isn't!" said Nora. "I don't want anybody in my bed. I don't want anybody in my bedroom. I don't want anybody to touch my things. I don't want anybody——"

"But darling," said Mother, "you shouldn't feel that way. Why, you'll never be happy in life if you just keep all your things to yourself. Try sharing them for once, and see how very, very happy you will be."

"I won't!" cried Nora, pouting. "I won't have anybody in my bed."

With that, she stormed out of the room and slammed the door.

Mother folded up the letter and finished her breakfast alone, doing a little thinking at the same time.

Three days later Brenda and her mother arrived. It was a very cold welcome the little girl received from Nora.

"Now, Mother," Nora whispered as the visitors were led upstairs, "remember, I don't want her in my room."

Mother didn't even seem to listen. Opening Nora's bedroom door, she said, "Here you are, Brenda. I know you'll be glad to sleep in here with Nora while you are visiting with us."

"Oh, yes!" cried Brenda, looking around at the spotless room with its pretty yellow curtains, its green carpet, and its beautiful furniture. "This will be just wonderful. I know I'll be very happy here. Thank you so much."

Nora glared, and when Mother had closed the door, she said to Brenda, "Well, if you have to stay in my room, you'll have to be very careful of my things. You mustn't touch one of them unless I tell you."

"I won't; really, I won't," said Brenda. "I'll be so happy just looking at them."

"Remember," said Nora, "when we go to bed tonight, don't you dare take up too much room, or I don't know what I'll do to you. I'm not used to having anyone in my bed."

"Oh, I won't take up too much room," laughed Brenda, wondering whether Nora was really serious about it. "I'll just be as small as a peanut. You'll see."

But Nora *was* serious. She couldn't stand having anybody in her own precious room, not even Brenda; and Brenda, she had to admit, was rather a nice girl after all.

At last bedtime arrived and the two mothers came in to kiss their little girls good night.

There they lay, as far apart as possible, Brenda at one edge of the bed, Nora at the other.

"I hope you have a lovely, comfortable sleep," said Nora's mother, "and wake up very happy in the morning."

"I won't sleep a wink," said Nora.

"I will," said Brenda; "I'm so cozy in here."

"Well, good night, dears."

"Good night!"

The two mothers went downstairs, smiling at each other and wondering what would happen next.

They did not have long to wait.

"Get over," said Nora. "You touched me with your foot."

"Sorry," said Brenda. "I didn't mean to."

A pause.

"Move over, can't you!" snapped Nora. "You are too near the middle."

"All right." And Brenda moved.

Silence for a while.

"Nora," whispered Brenda.

"Yes. What do you want?"

"Did you ever have a pillow fight?"

"No. Why?"

"It's lots of fun. I've had them with my brother ever so many times."

"What do you do?"

"S-sh! I'll tell you." And Brenda, in awed whispers, told just how it was done.

Nora was interested. She had never had anybody to play a game like this with her.

Pretty soon they were both sitting up in bed; then standing up.

"I'll start," said Brenda.

Wallop! Down came the pillow on Nora's head.

"Ouch!" cried Nora, stepping backward.

"Now you try!" said Brenda.

"I'll try," said Nora as she brought her pillow down on Brenda as hard as she could, almost falling off the bed as she did so.

The fun was on.

Bang! Bang! Bang!

Wallop! Wallop! Wallop!

Crash!

Brenda had fallen onto the floor, but in a moment she was up again and the two were banging away with the pillows, sometimes missing, sometimes hitting, as they staggered all over the springy mattress. And so the fun went merrily on, amid shrieks of laughter, until they were all out of breath.

"There seem to be strange noises upstairs," said Nora's mother. "I wonder what is happening."

"I wonder," said Brenda's mother.

Bang! Bang! Bang!

Wallop! Wallop! Wallop!

"Perhaps we had better go and see what they are doing up there."

Both of the mothers looked worried as they jumped up and hurried to the stairs.

Suddenly all the noise upstairs stopped.

◀ Painting by Vernon Nye

Nora and Brenda had a thrilling time pillow fighting till Brenda fell off the bed.

"S-sh!" cried Brenda.
"They're coming! Quick, get
into bed!"

There was a scramble under the sheets.

"Hug me tight!" said Brenda. "And let's pretend we're
asleep."

A moment later they were both lying in the middle of the
bed, the covers over them, breathing deeply, their eyes tight
shut.

"The darlings," said the two mothers as they looked down
at the "sleeping" pair, close in each other's arms.

"I knew they'd be happy together," said Brenda's mother
to Nora's mother.

"Er—yes," said Nora's mother, "I hoped they would be,
too."

And they were.

"I like Brenda so much," said Nora one day. "She's such good fun, and we have the most glorious time together. You should have seen her giving my best doll a bath today. You would have screamed, Mother; really you would."

"So you're glad that she came, after all?" asked Mother, with a strange smile playing about the corners of her mouth.

"Of course," said Nora. "I always wanted her to come. Really I did!"

And Mother smiled again.

STORY 32

Overcoming Temptation

"YOU LOOK SAD, BESSIE," said Faith, as her little friend came walking up the garden path. "Why, you've been crying! What's wrong?"

"You'd cry too if your mommy had spanked you as hard as mine has just spanked me," said Bessie, sniffing a little and rubbing a certain part of her rather dolefully!

"I'm sorry," said Faith, "but what did you do to deserve it?"

Bessie was silent a moment. She really didn't like to say anything about it.

"Come along, now, own up," said Faith in a friendly way.

"I told my mommy a fib and she found out," replied Bessie after a moment's silence.

"Oh, dear," said Faith, who was a very good little girl, "but you shouldn't tell fibs, Bessie. It always gets people into trouble. My mother says so; and in the Bible it says, 'Be sure your sin will find you out.'"

"But I can't help it sometimes," said Bessie. "I seem to tell a fib without really meaning to; and then, of course, I have to tell another one to cover up the first one, and it gets worse

and worse until Mommy finds out."

"You should learn how not to tell fibs and do naughty things," said Faith solemnly.

"Is there some way?" asked Bessie, now eager to hear Faith's secret.

"Oh, yes there is," replied Faith. "Want me to tell you what it is?"

"Oh, yes," said Bessie. "I'd like to know. Really I would."

"It's very easy," went on Faith. "First of all I ask Jesus to come into my heart. You can do that, too, Bessie, when you say your prayers at night."

"Yes, I think I can," said Bessie; "but what next?"

"Well," said Faith, "that is the biggest part of it. You see, when Satan comes knocking on the door of my heart to tempt me to tell fibs or to say unkind things or hurt animals or be rude to Mamma, then I run straight to tell Jesus. 'Jesus,' I say, 'there's naughty Satan knocking on the door again.' And Jesus says, 'All right, dear, you leave him to Me.'

"Immediately Jesus goes to the door and opens it; and when Satan sees *Him* coming, he says, 'Excuse me, I've called at the wrong house.' Then Satan runs away as fast as he can, and the temptation is all gone."

"That's a great idea," said Bessie; "and it does sound easy. Do you think Jesus will help *me* like that?"

"I'm sure He will," said Faith, "if you will ask Him."

Bessie did ask Jesus that very night. The very next time she found herself about to do what Satan was tempting her to do, she asked Jesus to drive Satan away. And she found that it worked.

33

When Dick Ran Away

DICK WAS UPSET AGAIN. In fact, it seemed that he was always getting upset about something. If he did not get his own way all the time, he would carry on in the most hateful manner. And if anyone corrected him, he would either snarl an angry reply, or else wander off into some corner and sulk.

When in these very bad moods he would mutter threats about running away from home. Although he was only 10 years old, he had a very big opinion of himself and was quite sure that he was well able to look after himself anywhere. That he owed his father and mother anything for all their loving care for him never seemed to enter his mind. He only wanted to get away from all control, away to some place where he would be able to do just as he pleased.

He was thinking these thoughts now. Daddy had asked him to mow the lawn just as he had planned to go out and play ball with the boy next door. How he hated mowing the lawn! Why should he mow the lawn? He wished there were no lawn to cut. He would give anything to get away from the sight of it. But he did mow it, seething with rebellion.

169

◀ Gib Crockett, Artist

That afternoon his wishes were crossed again. Several times, in fact. As a result he became rude and cross, and finished up with a good spanking and being sent early to bed. He did not say his prayers, and instead of going to sleep, he planned what seemed an exciting dash for liberty. He would get up when everyone else had gone to bed, creep out of the house, and run far, far away. He was not quite sure where he would go, or what he would do when he got there. He had only one desire—to get away where there would be no lawn to mow and where he wouldn't have to give up things for his brothers and sisters, nor be expected to do what he was told.

At last, when all was still, and he felt sure that everyone must be fast asleep, he decided to put his plan into action.

So he crawled softly out of bed, put on his clothes very quietly, took his billfold out of the drawer—he was very proud of this billfold, for it contained a whole dollar—and crept silently out of his room.

As he passed the bed where his baby brother was lying asleep, it occurred to him that he would never see little Tiny again, so he bent over and kissed him. A strange lump came into his throat, and he couldn't swallow very well. He kissed Tiny twice, and then went out of the room. Going past the

room where Daddy and Mother were asleep, he thought he
would like to say good-by to Mother anyway. He wasn't quite
sure about Daddy, because he had made him mow the lawn.
But he wouldn't like it if he couldn't see Mother again.

He began to wonder whether he should run away after all.
Then the old, hard spirit came back, and he went downstairs.
Very quietly he unlocked the front door, and went out into
the cool night air.

He stopped on the doorstep. This was hardly what he had
dreamed about. It was too dark for one thing, and too chilly
for another. Bed began to seem very nice. Perhaps, after all,
it would be better to go back.

But no, he wouldn't. He closed the door. There was a snap!
and he realized that he couldn't go back now even if he
wanted to. That wasn't a nice feeling at all. He wished he
hadn't let the door close quite so tightly.

It was done now, however, and he must go. He went down to the front gate and out into the street. There was nobody about. All was very quiet and still. The sky was black, and the only light came from the street lights. It was all rather frightening. Dick didn't like it a bit. If the door weren't locked, he told himself, he would go back to bed.

He walked some distance down the street, and as the cold night air cooled his fevered mind, he began to realize more and more what a foolish enterprise he had started on. "If the boys at school get to hear about this," he said to himself, "they'll tease me for the rest of the year." The very thought of such a thing made him turn around suddenly and make for home as fast as he could.

He had not gone far, however, when he nearly jumped out of his skin as a heavy hand was laid on his shoulder and a strange voice spoke to him.

"What are you doing out at this time of night?" asked the policeman.

Dick was paralyzed with fright. He had not expected this.
Words would not come. He merely struggled to get free.

"You'd better come along with me," said the policeman.
"You've been up to some mischief, it seems."

"I haven't, I haven't," gasped Dick. "I've made a mistake,
that's all, please, sir."

"I should think you have made a mistake, being out here
at one o'clock in the morning. You can tell me all about it
when we get down to the station."

"You're not going to take me to the police station, are
you?" cried Dick, more frightened still. "Let me go home! I
want to go home."

"You'll go home, all right," said the policeman, "after we
have had a little chat."

And so poor Dick found himself for the first time in his
life on his way to the police station!

There he was asked more questions in ten minutes than
any teacher had ever asked him at school. He was frightened,
wondering what the policeman was going to do with him and
what his daddy would say.

How he wished he had never started out on such a foolish
venture! Finally, the policeman took him home. How very
small poor Dick felt! What a homecoming! What would the
others say?

Daddy, in his pajamas, opened the door. It startled him to
see Dick there, and with a policeman!

"What in the world!" he began.

The policeman explained and departed, smiling. Dick
jumped into Daddy's arms and hugged him, pajamas and all.
They didn't say much to each other, but just walked up the
stairs like that to tell Mother all about it.

When Dick got up for breakfast that morning he found
his favorite food—crispy waffles, with delicious applesauce
—waiting for him. Mother had it ready because, she said,
her little prodigal had returned, so she surely had to kill
the fatted calf. (See the story in Volume 1 called "The Boy
Who Ran Away From Home.")

And as for Dick, he said very earnestly that he had run
away for the last time in his life, and that he certainly
wouldn't even think about doing so again.

◀ Painting by Jack White

Is This
the Morning?

HOW THAT YOUNGEST BOY of mine used to love the sea! You should have seen him holding the wheel of one of those little motorboats they have at some seaside resorts. Was he happy!

When I took him in a big speedboat one day and left him all alone on the back seat, the look of perfect bliss on his face was something wonderful to behold.

Many years ago, as we were driving through British Columbia, I happened to say that we might be going on a big steamer soon.

Alas, for our peace!

"When are we going on the big steamer, Daddy?" he asked. "How many funnels does it have? Will it have lots of smoke? Will it go very fast? Will we go far, far away? Will it be the *Queen Mary?*"

But the chief question was always, "When are we going, Daddy? Will it be tomorrow?"

"No," I said, "not tomorrow."

"Then how soon?"

"Very, very soon."

176

"Oh, dear, I can hardly wait!"

So the days went by, with the same questions being asked over and over again, the inquiry always ending with that plaintive plea, "Will it be very soon now?"

Purposely I did not tell him the exact day for fear he would become too excited about it. So I kept saying, "Soon, very soon now."

Then one day we crossed the border into the United States, and drove to Seattle. There we stayed for the night, so as to be in good time to catch the boat in the morning.

But we did not tell the boy. Oh, dear, no. He wouldn't have slept a wink. Neither would we.

So when he asked again, as he went to sleep, "Are we going on the boat soon, Daddy?" I said, "Oh, yes, *very*, very soon now," at which his weary little head fell on the pillow as though he were quite content. Little did he realize that he was so near to the goal of his dreams.

Now, whether or not it was because he had slept within a quarter of a mile of that ship I cannot say, but he awoke early the next day with the certain conviction in his heart that the great moment had arrived.

Rubbing his little eyes and looking up earnestly into his

2-12

mother's face, he said with an eagerness I shall never forget, *"Is this the morning?"*

"Oh, yes," I said, responding to the light of hope and joy blazing in his eyes. "Yes, this is the morning. This is the day you have been waiting for so long. Today we shall go on the big steamer and see the masts and the funnels and all the smoke and things, and ride over the great waves."

Is this the morning?

Ever since then the words have rung in my ears like a chime of lovely bells.

I have thought of all the people who have been waiting such a long, long time for the glorious morning of eternity, and how happy they will be when it breaks.

There are some people alive today who have been waiting nearly a hundred years for Jesus to come. They have not known the time of His coming, but, oh, how they have longed for it! And they have comforted their old hearts by saying, It must be soon now; there's not much longer to wait!

What joy will be theirs "in the morning"!

I have thought, too, of all the people who have endured sickness and pain, blindness and deafness, and all sorts of dreadful injuries—and how glad they will be "in the morning" when Jesus comes back to open the eyes of the blind, to unstop the ears of the deaf, and to make the lame man leap as a hart! How wonderful it will be to see their joy as they are suddenly healed by His wondrous power, never to be sick again!

I have thought also of all those who have put up with great hardship and poverty, rarely ever seeing trees or

flowers or the beauty of the country or the sea—and what 179
pure delight will be theirs "in the morning" when they discover that they will never be poor again, that Jesus has come to bring them riches enough to last forever and ever, and food enough\ so they will never know hunger again; oh, yes, and when they find that He has planned for them a new heaven and a new earth more lovely than any they ever imagined!

I have thought, too, of all the exiles, the people who have been driven from their homes and countries by cruel tyrants, and how they must have cried again and again as they wandered homeless over the earth, and how thrilled they will be "in the morning" to find that Jesus has made ready for them the very mansions that long ago He promised to prepare for His children, a home that shall never pass away.

I have thought, also, of all the children of God who have gone to sleep in death through all the ages since sin first entered this old world, and how marvelous it will be when Jesus comes to wake them from their long slumber.

Hundreds and thousands of them were loving fathers and mothers who passed away, longing for their children; and countless others were children who died, longing to see their parents again; and one day soon upon their waiting ears will fall the voice of Jesus calling them from the grave.

Can you not hear them all crying in glad and happy surprise, "Jesus, *is this the morning?*"

What a glad reunion there will be that day!

Many will have been martyrs for Jesus—men, women, and children who chose to be tortured and killed rather than give up their faith in Him. Lots and lots of them perished miserably in dungeons, waiting patiently for deliverance that never came.

Can you not hear them crying, almost frantic with joy, as the Master for whom they gave up so much bends over them in tender love and calls them from the tomb to spend eternity

◀ Photo by J. Byron Logan   Painting by Harry Anderson © by Review and Herald ▶

Christ points all of His children to the bright morning when He will come back to earth to take them with Him to heaven.

with Him, "O Jesus, is this the morning for which we have waited so long?"

Some people talk about the coming of Jesus as a day of darkness, gloom, and misery, but for all who love Him it is going to be the happiest day in history. That's why the apostle Paul calls it "the blessed hope." It's going to be the most

wonderful, the most glorious, and the most joyous event that ever happened.

Every one of us should be looking forward to it with the keenest joy, just as Jesus Himself must be longing, too, for the great day to dawn.

In my front garden, down by the gate, there used to be the trunk of a dead pepper tree. The top was flat and made a little seat, and there was a step so that one could climb up onto it.

For years this was my youngest boy's seat, where he would sit and wait for his daddy to come home.

It used to make going home so thrilling to think he would be there. When I was still a long way off he would see me and there would be yelling and excited waving of hands.

And it seems to me that this is how Jesus would have us await His coming—sitting high up on the pepper tree, as it were, looking eagerly down the road, "waiting and watching for Him"

And I believe that just as I would take up my little boy and hug him because he was waiting there at the gate for me, so Jesus will gather us into His everlasting arms of love and tell us He is glad we did the same for Him.

Then in that glorious day we will all go in together to partake of "the marriage supper of the Lamb," and to hear His kind voice say to everybody, " 'Come, O blessed of my Father, inherit the kingdom prepared for you from the foundation of the world' " (Matthew 25:34. R.S.V.).*

And it will all be so wonderful, so unbelievably beautiful, that we shall cry out in rapture once more—

"Is this the morning?"

And I am sure the angels will join with us in a wonderful song of joyful assurance.

*All R.S.V. texts are from *The Holy Bible, Revised Standard Version,* Thomas Nelson and Sons, New York, 1952.

Painting by Harry Anderson © by Review and Herald ▶

Jesus' people will be looking for His coming with the keenest joy.